PELICAN BOOKS

A507

THE COMMON SENSE OF SCIENCE

J. BRONOWSKI

J. BRONOWSKI

The Common Sense of Science

PENGUIN BOOKS

Penguin Books Ltd, Harmondsworth, Middlesex
AUSTRALIA: Penguin Books Pty Ltd, 762 Whitehorse Road
Mitcham, Victoria

—

First published by Heinemann 1951
Published in Pelican Books 1960
Reprinted 1960, 1962

—

Made and Printed in Great Britain
by Spottiswoode, Ballantyne & Co. Ltd.
London and Colchester
Set in Monotype Baskerville

Contents

CHAPTER I

Science and Sensibility

I

I CAME to England when I was twelve, and when I landed I could speak, rather badly, two words of English which I had learned on the channel boat. I did not read English at all easily for two or three years after. The first writers in whom I was able to distinguish what my patient schoolmasters called style were, I remember, Macaulay and Joseph Conrad. I do not remember now whether at that time I was also able to distinguish between their styles. I read greedily, with excitement, with affection, with a perpetual sense of discovering a new and, I slowly realized, a great literature. But I was handicapped then, and I have been ever since, by the disorderly way in which I fell upon my masterpieces: Dickens cheek by jowl with Aphra Behn and Bernard Shaw, and elsewhere leaving tracts of neglected literature by the century. To this day I have not read the Waverley novels, and in consequence I have remained rather insensitive to historical romance, particularly if much of the conversation is in dialect.

I make these confessions because they seem to me to bear on many stories besides my own. The difficulties which I had are not mine alone, and they are not in any special way literary difficulties. On the contrary, what now strikes me about them is their likeness to the trouble which other people have with science. At bottom my difficulties in facing a strange literature are precisely the difficulties which all intelligent people today have in trying to make some order out of modern science.

We live surrounded by the apparatus of science: the
Diesel engine and the experiment, the bottle of aspirins
and the survey of opinion. We are hardly conscious of
them; but behind them we are becoming conscious of a
new importance in science. We are coming to understand
that science is not a haphazard collection of manufacturing techniques carried out by a race of laboratory
dwellers with acid-yellow fingers and steel-rimmed spec-
tacles and no home life. Science, we are growing aware,
is a method and a force of its own, which has its own
meaning and style and its own sense of excitement. We
are aware now that somewhere within the jungle of
valves and formulae and shining glassware lies a content;
lies, let us admit it, a new culture.

How are we to reach that culture, across its jargons,
and translate it into a language which we know? The
difficulties of the layman are my boyhood difficulties.
He opens his newspaper and there stands a revelation in
capitals: THE ELECTRONIC BRAIN, or SUPERSONIC
FLIGHT, or *Is there life on Mars?* But capitals or italics,
the revelation remains in code for him. The language is
as strange to him as *The Anatomy of Melancholy* was to me
at fifteen. He has only the smallest vocabulary: a smat-
tering from other popular articles, schoolboy memories
of the stinks lab, and a few names of scientists sprinkled
at random across history. His history, which might have
given an order to it all, is the most maddening of his
uncertainties. I knew no English history, and therefore
I could not make sense of literary development. How
well I recall the helplessness with which I faced a list of
names such as Marlowe and Coleridge and H. G. Wells.
I could not make any historical order of them. It is hard
to visualize my difficulty; yet just this is the difficulty
which every reader meets when he sees the names of
Napier, Humphry Davy, and Rutherford. These three

scientists were contemporaries of the three writers, and they were by no means lesser men.

2

A knowledge of history of course, even the history of science, will not do duty for science. But it gives us the backbone in the growth of science, so that the morning headline suddenly takes its place in the development of our world. It throws a bridge into science from whatever humanist interest we happen to stand on. And it does so because it asserts the unity not merely of history but of knowledge. The layman's key to science is its unity with the arts. He will understand science as a culture when he tries to trace it in his own culture.

It has been one of the most destructive modern prejudices that art and science are different and somehow incompatible interests. We have fallen into the habit of opposing the artistic to the scientific temper; we even identify them with a creative and a critical approach. In a society like ours which practises the division of labour there are of course specialized functions, as matters of convenience. As a convenience, and only as a convenience, the scientific function is different from the artistic. In the same way the function of thought differs from, and complements, the function of feeling. But the human race is not divided into thinkers and feelers, and would not long survive the division.

Much of this quarrel between science and soul was trumped up by the religious apologists of Queen Victoria's day, who were anxious to find science materialistic and unspiritual. The sneer that science is only critical came from others. It was made by the timid and laboured artists of the nineties in order that they might by comparison appear to be creative and intuitive. Yet this finesse could not hide their own knowledge that the best minds were already being drawn to the more adventurous practice of the new sciences: a movement which Peacock had foreseen seventy-five years before in *The Four Ages of Poetry*.

The arts and the sciences ever since have been in competition for the most lively young brains. This competition is itself the clearest evidence that good minds can fulfil themselves as well in one as in the other. Here in fact is one of the few psychological discoveries of our generation to which we can hold with a reasonable certainty: that the general configuration of intelligence factors which distinguish the bright from the dull is the same in one man as another, in the humanist as in the scientist. We are divided by schooling and experience; and we do differ, though we differ less, in our aptitudes; but below these, we share a deeper basis of common ability. This is why I write with confidence for laymen and scientists, because the reader who is interested in any activity which needs thought and judgement is almost certainly a person to whom science can be made to speak. It is not he who is deaf, but the specialists who have been dumb – the specialists in the arts as well as the sciences.

Many people persuade themselves that they cannot understand mechanical things, or that they have no head for figures. These convictions make them feel enclosed and safe, and of course save them a great deal of trouble. But the reader who has a head for anything at all is pretty sure to have a head for whatever he really wants to put his mind to. His interest, say in mathematics, has usually been killed by routine teaching, exactly as the literary interest of most scientists (and, for that matter, of most non-scientists) has been killed by the set book and the Shakespeare play. Few people would argue that those whose taste for poetry has not survived the School Certificate are fundamentally insensitive to poetry. Yet they cheerfully write off the large intellectual pleasures of science as if they belonged only to minds of a special cast. Science is not a special sense. It is as wide as the literal meaning of its name: knowledge. The notion of the specialized mind is by comparison as modern as the specialized man, 'the scientist', a word which is only a hundred years old.

3

Therefore I have in mind as I write a reader who is less interested in the sciences than he is in science. There was in the last century a tradition of self-teaching in the Mechanics' Institutes which in its time was a just cause for pride. But the tradition is gone and its going now is not a loss, because the interest in science has widened. We are all aware of the widening. Those who hanker after a knowledge of science today are not looking for technical information. They are no longer unfortunates who would have liked to work in a laboratory too, if fate had not sent them into a mill at twelve. I take it for granted that those who take up this book are well content with what they know and do, and are not thinking of themselves vicariously as the white-coated hero of a second feature about the discovery of Compound E. And I do not assume that they must necessarily be fascinated by the marvels of the electron microscope or of radio-active iodine. I think of them as people aware that the world into which they were born is changing during their lifetime, and who have about this change the same curiosity which they have about what is new in their closer neighbourhood – in literature or the arts or local politics or the business of the tennis club.

Few people today are really in doubt about the scale and the lasting importance of this change. But many people push it to the back of their minds, resolutely or in embarrassment. And much of the time they fear to face it, because they are afraid to acknowledge that this movement is changing their lives, is washing away the landmarks of their familiar world, rising round their values, and in the end drowning the selves which must last them their lifetime. Yet these fears are less fears of the social change which science is working than simple personal fears. They are afraid, we are all afraid of being left out. We are afraid that something is happening which we shall not be able to understand and which will shut us out from the fellowship of the brighter and younger people.

These fears I believe are groundless. I believe that it is easy for a man who likes conversation and to read the second leader now and again to be comfortable with the large ideas of science: as easy as it is for a scientist to have a fancy for biography. The difficulties are those of language and the personal fear of what is unfamiliar. These are merely fed by those enthusiastic scientists who write as if the layman were to be pitied, and treat him as an erring would-be scientist who ought to be converted to an interest in the nucleus. I have no such reader in mind. I think of my readers, scientists as well as laymen, as balanced people who see about them the world in movement, and who want to know enough about the forces of science outside their own neighbourhood to assess their part in that profound and total movement of history.

4

Many people affect to believe that science has progressively strangled the arts, or distorted them into some unpleasant 'modern' form; and therefore that the arts can be revived only by throwing over science. Often of course this is merely an elderly sentiment in favour of the art of our younger days, and the real scapegoat is not science but change. But even where the sentiment is less partial, it springs from a misunderstanding of progress in art and science. Science today is plainly more powerful than, let us say, in the time of Isaac Newton. Against this, the arts today seldom reach the height of, say, his contemporary John Dryden. It is therefore tempting to conclude that science continually outgrows its older ideas, while great literature remains permanent. But this is a hopeless muddle of concepts. Newtons are no more plentiful today than Drydens; and the work of Newton continues to stand to modern science in precisely the relation that the prose of Dryden stands to modern prose. Dryden and Newton each revealed a wholly new set of possibilities in their forms of knowledge. Both are classics in this sense, that they were at once pioneers and men of great achievement. And neither is a classic in any other sense.

The belief that science destroys culture is sometimes supported by historical statements that the arts have flourished only when the sciences have been neglected. This thesis is so directly contrary to history that I find it difficult to begin to debate it. What is this golden age of art untarnished by the breath of rude mechanics? Where did it exist? In the East? The civilizations of Egypt, of India, and of the Arabs belie it. The only oriental poet at all well known in England, Omar Khayyam, was a Persian astronomer. In the West? The culture of the West begins in Greece; and in the great age of Greece, art and science penetrate one another more closely than in any modern age. Pythagoras lived before Aeschylus had created Greek drama. Socrates taught when that drama was at its greatest; and is Socrates to be claimed by art or science? And Plato, who did not tolerate poets in his ideal state, was a scholar when Aristophanes closed the eyes of Greek drama. The example of these men in science as much as in art set the modern world afire in the Renaissance. And the type and symbol of Renaissance man was from the beginning and remains Leonardo da Vinci, painter, sculptor, mathematician, and engineer. No man has shown more strikingly the universality and the unity of the intellect.

In England we put the golden age into the reign of Queen Elizabeth; and that characteristically was an age of commercial and industrial as well as of literary invention. Voyagers and adventurers like Sir Walter Ralegh were the Leonardos of that age; and Ralegh's own circle, which turned Christopher Marlowe into a rationalist, was dominated by a mathematician and astronomer, Thomas Hariot. For navigation is dependent on astronomy; it went hand in hand with the new speculations about the world and the solar system; and in turn, the voyages of the great navigators inspired the literature of Elizabethan England. The worlds of art and of science and the physical world unfolded then together. It was not by accident that the first table of logarithms was published within a few years of the First Folio.

Sixty years after the death of Elizabeth, another great age ripened in England, the age of Restoration literature. I shall have a great deal to say about that in this book, because one symbol of the age is the founding of what has remained the most important scientific society in the world. The meeting which founded it on 28 November 1660 opened with a lecture on astronomy, and the lecture was given by Christopher Wren the architect. The society was given its name, the Royal Society, and its motto by the most enthusiastic of its founders. He was John Evelyn the diarist. When the society wanted to encourage the use of simple and lucid prose, it appointed a committee which included a fellow of the society with a special gift for such writing. He was the poet John Dryden.

5

The golden ages of literature were in fact times of greatness when science and the arts went forward hand in hand. Has all this come to an end? Literary critics say Yes, it ended in England at the Industrial Revolution, somewhere between 1760 and 1800. Yet these critics date the Romantic Revival from some point between the death of Collins in 1759, which meant so much to Wordsworth, and the publication of the *Lyrical Ballads* in 1798. These two sets of dates are almost identical, and can it be reasonable to keep them in separate compartments of the mind? Is it really tenable to think of the Industrial Revolution as a kind of death? It gave our world its structure. It turned science from astronomy to what are essentially its modern interests, which hinge on the use of mechanical power. And it created in the romantic poets and the reformers what has remained our sensibility.

I say created our sensibility, although of course I have pointed only to the coincidence of dates: that Blake and Coleridge and Wilberforce were after all contemporaries of Arkwright and James Watt. Against this, those who hold the illusion that pre-industrial England was more sensitive and cultured, point to the misery of the manufacturing age: women in mines, children in factories, the disasters of enclosure, famine, the Napoleonic wars, and political reaction. These were very terrible evils, but they are evils far older than 1800 and the machines. The labour of women and children for endless hours in their own homes is a commonplace in Defoe's journals in 1725. Yet the Augustan optimists of his day did not see it as matter for protest. But in the factory these evils became naked and public; and the driving force for reform came from the men of the mill, from Robert Owen and the elder Peel. We today are scandalized that boys went on climbing in chimneys for nearly eighty years after the heart-rending poems which Blake wrote about them around 1790; the last of the climbing boys, Joseph Lawrence, is still alive as I write. But the boys had been climbing for a hundred years before Blake without a line of protest from Addison or Gay or Dr Johnson. In their broad Augustan day, Scottish miners were legally still serfs, just as the miners of Greece had always been slaves; and neither civilization thought anything amiss. So today in China and India and other countries with few machines, life is brutal and laborious, and sensibility is unknown; I have seen it so myself, under the rusty thin surface of mechanization in Japan, for women and animals alike. It was the engine, it was the horsepower which created consideration for the horse; and the Industrial Revolution which created our sensibility.

6

Science changes our values in two ways. It injects new ideas into the familiar culture. And it subjects it to the pressure of technical change, in the way I have just been describing, until the whole basis of our culture has imperceptibly been remade. The invention of printing does not seem to bear very directly on the content of poetry. But when a poem can be read and read again, it is natural that the interest shifts from the rhythm to the meaning and the allusion. So the invention of photography has made the painter and the patron lose interest in the likeness and transfer it to some more formal pattern. Our whole sensibility has been re-created by such subtle shifts.

Science and the arts today are not as discordant as many people think. The difficulties which we all have as intelligent amateurs in following modern literature and music and painting are not unimportant. They are one sign of the lack of a broad and general language in our culture. The difficulties which we have in understanding the basic ideas of modern science are signs of the same lack. Science and the arts shared the same language at the Restoration. They no longer seem to do so today. But the reason is that they share the same silence: they lack the same language. And it is the business of each of us to try to remake that one universal language which alone can unite art and science, and layman and scientist, in a common understanding.

CHAPTER 2

The Scientific Revolution and the Machine

I

THERE are three creative ideas which, each in its turn, have been central to science. They are the idea of order, the idea of causes, and the idea of chance. This book is concerned largely with these ideas. I begin at what is perhaps the most fugitive of the three, the idea of order.

None of these ideas is peculiar to science, and the idea of order least of all. They have applications to science; but all three are of course older than these applications. All are wider and deeper than the techniques in which science expresses them. They are common sense ideas; by which I mean that they are generalizations which we all make from our daily lives, and which we go on using to help us run our lives.

Unhappily, common sense has no recorded history. We often suppose indeed that it has no development, and that what we call common sense today has always been common sense to everybody – which certainly is not true.

Science records all this more conveniently. Science has a history in which the growth of these ideas can be traced plainly. More than this, we can in that history detect the moments of surpassing interest, when the common sense ideas were being formed afresh. Such a moment is now plain in the history of the seventeenth century. That age, which made Newton and which Newton made, was a climax and a fresh beginning in English science. And I go directly to Newton himself because nothing so reveals that age as the remarkable character of its greatest man.

2

No man of science, no man of thought has ever equalled the reputation of Isaac Newton. No other man has made so deep a mark on his time and on our world unless he has been a man of action, a Cromwell or a Napoleon. Like Cromwell's and like Napoleon's, Newton's achievement was made possible by the coincidence, or better by the interplay of personality and opportunity. Each of these men, the man of thought as well as the men of action, entered history at a moment of social instability. Newton was born during Cromwell's revolution in the troubled 1640s; he was eighteen at the Restoration in 1660; and he published the *Principia* during the intrigues which ended by bringing William of Orange to England in the revolution of 1688. These are the moments when the powerful mind or the forceful character feels the ferment of the times, when his thoughts quicken, and when he can inject into the uncertainties of others the creative ideas which will strengthen them with purpose. At such a moment the man who can direct others, in thought or in action, can remake the world.

Newton was such a personality. That complicated and nevertheless direct mind, that imperturbable engine of thought has stamped its mark on everything he did. The stamp is Newton's style, and the style and the content are one; both are projections of the same single-minded personality.

Science is not an impersonal construction. It is no less, and no more, personal than any other form of communicated thought. This book is not less scientific because my manner is personal, and I make no apology for it. Science searches the common experience of people; and it is made by people, and it has their style. The style of a great man marks not only his own work, but through it the work of others for generations. The style of Newton's work as much as the content dominated science for two centuries, and in that time shaped its manner and its matter. But style is not the monopoly of the great, nor is its appreciation a vintage reserved for experts. The schoolboy who can tell a neat proof from a dull one knows the style, and takes pleasure in it. Indeed, he finds it easier to appreciate the style of science than the style of Shakespeare.

I cannot hope to transmit that style, its feeling and its detail, at this remove. It cannot be bought, canned and dehydrated, on pages ten and eleven of somebody's history of world knowledge, either in the chapters on science or on Shakespeare. We all understand that Shakespeare, the whole Shakespeare, cannot be got out of any book but his own collected works. So if we want the whole Newton, the man and the manner, the large nose and the strong thumb-print of his style, then we must read the *Principia* and the *Opticks*. Only in this way will we get the personality and the movement of the work, the massive ease and the fluent assurance which the *Opticks* shares strikingly with *Antony and Cleopatra*.

But we need not therefore come to a dead stop on aesthetics. After all few of us value the style so highly that we cannot bear to read Balzac and Stendhal in translation, and even Flaubert and Proust. Few of us certainly would learn French only in order to preserve this aesthetic Puritanism. And in the same way we must be content with science in translation. The science of an age, like its art or its music, has a style, yes. But it has a content and a structure too, larger than the work of any one man, within which the work of its men takes shape and meaning. Shakespeare was one of a group of playwrights, and he and they shared the expanding world of the Elizabethan voyagers and the patriotic adventures. Newton was one of the young discoveries of the Royal Society in its early days, in the restless setting which I have been describing. To know this does not of itself make us appreciate their achievement; and still less can such knowledge take the place of appreciation, in art or in science. But it does give us a context in which we can look beyond the single furrow of our own interest, into the whole fertile field of knowledge.

3

There never has been another moment in English history to equal the promise of that moment in the 1660s when the Royal Society was formally founded. And though it was less dramatic elsewhere, it was a high moment throughout Europe. The long tradition of astronomy in the seafaring nations was about to reach its climax, here with Newton, and in Holland with Huygens.

What was extraordinary about that moment at the Restoration? We all have a regard for Restoration times, and that in itself is something of a puzzle. What exactly commands the affection in which good King Charles II's day is held? Surely not the political and literary achievements which the history books quote. The most romantic Tory could not call Charles II a great king. Dryden was a great poet; nevertheless as a poet he does not rank with his predecessor Milton. As for the Restoration playwrights, by all means let us make the most of their hearty fun; but it hardly earns them a major place in English drama.

No, at bottom our regard for the period is sound because it rests on wider and less familiar achievements than these. They are scientific rather than literary achievements, but they are not specifically one or the other, any more than is Dryden's superb prose. They are the pioneer achievements of a liberal culture, and are part of a spontaneous widening of sympathy and interests throughout Europe. We can trace this even in the strange political conditions which made possible the recall of Charles II without bloodshed and with little vindictiveness after a long dictatorship born and perpetuated in blood and violence. And consider the circumstances in which, on Charles's return, the Royal Society was founded. Most of its leaders were professors of Puritan sympathies and some of them held chairs from which Cromwell had evicted the royalist holders for them. Indeed, the mathematician John Wallis owed his eminence to his skill in applying science to Cromwell's military needs: he was a pioneer in breaking enemy cyphers, and this has remained the traditional wartime service of mathematicians. Charles II cannot have relished these men, and he had no overpowering interest in science. Yet Evelyn persuaded him to give his name to their new-fangled society; and the literary men competed with them for places in it.

There is a parallel in the position of Huygens in the Académie Royale des Sciences in Paris. Christian Huygens was born in Holland in 1629. His father and his grandfather were diplomats in the service of the House of Orange. The family was friendly with Descartes, who during Huygens's youth was an exile in Holland. In the 1660s Louis XIV was already putting pressure on the House of Orange and a little later he invaded Holland. Yet Huygens, a Dutchman, a Protestant, and a Cartesian, was called to France to help found the Académie Royale in 1666, and he remained its senior official into the 1680s, when anti-Protestant policy at last became too strong for him.

Huygens's distinction and leadership were as important to the Académie as were those of Newton, who was thirteen years younger, to the Royal Society soon after.

He was not the equal of Newton as a scientist; he had not quite Newton's penetration and range in mathematics or in the principles of experiment. His temper was more that of the inventor and mechanic, and the English scientist most like him was Robert Hooke, curator of experiments and secretary to the Royal Society – a slightly fantastic character, whose dislike of Newton (and Newton's dislike of him) gave an air of extravagance to the scientific arguments of the times. Like Hooke, Huygens made fundamental improvements to the clock as an aid to astronomy. Huygens in effect invented the pendulum as a time-keeping mechanism; and Hooke invented the first passable escapement for the same purpose. The work of each of them, like Newton's and like every scientist's in that uprush of invention, covered an enormous field. Huygens discovered the rings of Saturn, and the formula for centrifugal force. He did important work in mechanics and optics, and one of his merits was that he made the young Leibnitz enthusiastic for these subjects.

I have remarked that these men were not scientists alone, nor was there a barrier between their interests and those of men of other skills. Artists, writers, and scientists shared their interests and their passions. In England the fellows of the Royal Society included Robert Boyle with the poet Denham, and Samuel Pepys with the mathematician Wallis; and Sir William Petty, and Edmund Waller, and John Aubrey. The Society was interested in mathematics and fossils, in mechanics and botany, and in practical subjects from metallurgy to the statistics of population. It had a single and a universal thirst, 'to improve natural knowledge by experiment'.

What was true of England was true of the continent of Europe. Let us take the world of Huygens as an example again, to show how all its culture was held together by the same interests. Huygens is remembered in the textbooks because he believed that light is a wave motion, and worked out the idea with success. Newton held the opposite view, that light is a stream of tiny pellets; and here Newton was wrong, although the matter is not quite a straightforward right or wrong. But the real interest of this is in recalling how wide was the influence of optics throughout the culture of the time, and widest in Holland. Huygens was a contemporary of Rembrandt, Spinoza, and the great naturalist Leeuwenhoek. Leeuwenhoek was an amateur maker of simple microscopes and was outstanding in his studies of minute nature by this mechanical and observational skill. Spinoza was a skilled lens grinder. He was a by-product of his profession (like the cobbler-poets of German tradition) but the profession gave life to Dutch discovery; Galileo himself had made his telescope in 1609 only after hearing that Dutch lens grinders could look into the distance by putting lenses together. It is not fanciful to link the daily work of these men to the attention to light which Huygens gave in his thought, and Rembrandt in his painting. Nor was this attention absent in England; the beautiful experiments with colours which Newton describes in his *Opticks* made as great an impression on painters and poets here. The landscape of the poets of the eighteenth century is far more brightly coloured than that of earlier poets. We do not always notice the sensuous flow of colours in Pope, perhaps because it springs from this forgotten interest in the spectrum. Yet Pope uses three or four times as many colour words as Shakespeare, and uses them about ten times as often.

About 1660 therefore, Europe was in the course of a great revolution in thought. This was the Scientific Revolution, and it reached into all forms of culture. We sometimes speak as if science has step by step squeezed other interests out of our culture, and is slowly strangling the traditional ways of thinking. Nothing of the kind. The Scientific Revolution in the seventeenth century was a universal revolution. Indeed it could not have begun unless there had already been a deep change in the attitude to everything natural and super-natural among thoughtful men. Puritanism in England and Protestant martyrdom on the continent are the religious traces of that change; Marvell and Molière mark it in the arts, and Cromwell's revolution and the wars of Louis XIV are its political traces. Nor, of course, were these changes in the climate of mind without practical antecedents. At bottom, all derive from the explosion of the rigid hierarchy of land and craft which was the medieval world, by the growth of trade and industry for profit. But this regress to first causes takes us too far from the Scientific Revolution itself.

What is important here is that the change of which the Royal Society and the Académie Royale were the visible symbols was wider and deeper than science, and had to be before such symbols could become real. Charles I and Louis XIII could not conceivably have blessed these societies; yet their successors found it natural because by the 1660s the societies embodied a larger shift. Charles II and Louis XIV were not encouraging science; they merely acquiesced in a universal change of outlook. There was indeed a reaction in the next century, and one so interesting that we shall need to look at it closely. And this reaction is what makes us think of the more recent progress of science as a wholly adverse conquest. But these are the minor eddies in the flow of history. The great flood was the seventeenth century. That was the time of change, the hanging moment of instability in which men like Cromwell and Newton could remake the world. They struck the world

like the Severn bore, and overthrew it instantly; but the
change in outlook, the untapped head of water, had long
been gathering. To see what happened about 1660, we
must look at the landscape of science and thought before
that time, and see what it looked like before the change
quickened it.

4

The whole structure of thought in the Middle Ages is one
which we find hard to grasp today. It was an orderly
structure, but the principles by which it was ordered
seem to us now outlandish and meaningless. Take such
a simple question as that which is said to have turned
Newton's mind to the problem of gravitation: Why does
an apple when it leaves the tree fall down to the ground?
The question had been asked often since the fourteenth
century, when the active and inquiring men of the Italian
Renaissance began to take an interest in the mechanical
world. For answer, they went back to one of the great
re-discoveries of the Arabs and the Renaissance, the
works of the Greek philosophers. To us, this answer
smacks of the most pompous tradition of philosophy, and
does less to explain the world than to shuffle it in a set
of tautologies. For the Middle Ages answered the
question about the apple in the tradition of Aristotle:
The apple falls down and not up because it is its nature
to fall down.

In putting it in this way, I have of course made a
caricature of the answer. I have done so not to make fun
of it but, on the contrary, in order to show that even in
this extravagantly naïve form, the answer is not really
childish. It would be childish only if it read 'This apple
falls down and not up because it is the nature of this
apple at this instant to fall down.' But this is not what
Aristotle said. He said that the particular apple falls

down now because it is the nature of all apples to fall down at all times. Simple as this notion may seem to us, it is in itself a bold and remarkable extension of the mind. The mere creation of a permanent class of apples, the mere generalization of the concept of apples, is an act of the first importance. Of course it is simple enough to make a class of identical objects such as pennies or the capital As in this book. But nature does not provide identical objects; on the contrary, these are always human creations. What nature provides is a tree full of apples which are all recognizably alike and yet are not identical: small apples and large ones, red ones and pale ones, apples with maggots and apples without. To make a statement about all these apples together, and about crab-apples, Orange Pippins, and Beauties of Bath, is the whole basis of reasoning.

This is so important that I must underline it. The action of putting things which are not identical into a group or class is so familiar that we forget how sweeping it is. The action depends on recognizing a set of things to be alike when they are not identical. We order them by what it is that we think they have in common, which means by something that we feel to be a likeness between them. Habit makes us think the likeness obvious; it seems to us obvious that all apples are somehow alike, or all trees, or all matter. Yet there are languages in the Pacific Islands in which every tree on the island has a name, but which have no word for tree. To these islanders, trees are not at all alike; on the contrary, what is important to them is that the trees are different. In the same islands men identify themselves with the totem of their clan, say with the parrot, and it seems to them plain that they are like parrots when to us the notion seems a mere artifice, and an outrageous one.

This ability to order things into likes and unlikes is, I

think, the foundation of human thought. And it is a human ability; we trace and to some extent inject the likeness, which is by no means planted there by nature for all to see. Our very example of Newton's apple shows this vividly. For Newton's instant insight, as he himself told it, was precisely to see the likeness which no one else had seen between the fall of the apple and the swing of the moon in her orbit round the earth. The theory of gravitation rests upon this; and familiar as the likeness now is to us, and obvious, it would have seemed merely fanciful to the Aristoteleans of the Middle Ages.

5

But, of course, the generalizations concealed within their answer did not stop at apples. What the Aristoteleans said was that the apple falls down and not up because it is the nature of earthy things always to fall down. They saw a likeness between all masses, and they used it to order the world around them into different categories of things, earthy, watery, airy, and fiery. It was a far-reaching theory, and it was applied to the body and the mind as well as to dead matter. But what interests us now is the kind of structure which it gave to the universe. In that structure, earthy things belonged to the earth; their natural resting place was the centre of the earth; and they fell to earth in their longing for that. What buoyed the universe and kept it from finding the state of dead rest in its natural centres was the tug of war between the elements, earthy matter carried off by the action of fire, water swept up in a rush of air. The universe lived by the tension between the elements, all at cross purposes because all in search of their different centres. It is a lively idea, and it is an order of nature based upon recognizable likes and unlikes. Yet to us it is now only a neat fancy; the likeness on which it is built seems to us to lie in inessentials; and very bluntly it seems to us not to understand at all how the world works.

The system of the Middle Ages, which had been taken from Aristotle, differs in two outstanding ways from anything that we expect of a physical system. First, it has quite different notions about matter: notions which are different in kind from ours. There are within that picture springs of action of a kind we would not dream of projecting into matter: springs of human action, where we see only the impersonal turning of a machine. Earth, water, air, and fire have natures which are at bottom human nature, and were recognized by those who made this picture as parts of human nature. What drives them is a kind of will, a mindless will perhaps, but still an obstinate animal will. Masses as it were wanted to find rest at the centre of the earth; air wanted to stream up. Abstractly Aristotle might hold that, given these natures of the elements, everything else goes on of itself. But in fact it was not meant as a mechanism or worked out as one. It grew from a view of nature as essentially animal, wilful, and alive.

Secondly, there was in the whole conception a kind of order which was really a hierarchy. Under it all runs the thought of nature as it ought to be: the order to which the great design strives, and in achieving which it would be transfigured and would come to rest. Everything reaches towards its centre, earthy things down and airy things up, because that is their stable and rightful place; yet reaching this they would come to rest, and the world would stop upon that stroke of midnight. We see how this chimes with the Greek picture of a world at rest from instant to instant; and also with the religious picture of the Middle Ages, that all worldly life is imperfection. The world is disorderly, and it seeks its order in the great ideal hierarchy of how it ought to be. And it ought to be a still perfection.

The whole picture is almost inconceivable to us. It is not inconceivable as a fable; on the contrary, as a fable it remains familiar and powerful, as we can see by looking it up for instance in the later poems of Yeats. What is inconceivable to us is that it should have been regarded in any way as doing what is asked of a scientific theory. It does not explain, we say, it does not hold together, it does not keep going, it does not make sense. We mean that this world in no way resembles the inhuman, mindless, and automatic machine which we think the world: a machine in which whatever happens does so only because something else happened before.

6

There in a sentence we have the difference between the outlook of, let us say (to make the example pointed), Leonardo da Vinci and Isaac Newton. Da Vinci was as great a mechanic and inventor as were Newton and his friends. Yet a glance at his notebooks shows us that what fascinated him about nature was its variety, its infinite adaptability, the fitness and the individuality of all its parts. By contrast what made astronomy a pleasure to Newton was its unity, its singleness, its model of a nature in which the diversified parts were mere disguises for the same blank atoms. And when da Vinci wanted an effect, he willed, he planned the means to make it happen: that was the purpose of his machines. But the machines of Newton (and he was a gifted experimenter) are means not for doing but for observing. He saw an effect, and he looked for its cause.

I have come thus upon the idea of causes, and made it plain that it is one face of the great division between the

Middle Ages and the Scientific Age. It would be possible to make this in itself the essential division; the plan is natural and convenient. We could say that the Middle Ages saw nature as a striving towards its own inner order; and that the Scientific Revolution overthrew this order and put in its place the mechanism of causes. But this does not go to the heart of the matter. On the one hand, all science, and indeed all thinking, starts from and rests upon notions of order; what marks the Middle Ages is that their order was always a hierarchy. And on the other hand, what marks the scientific view is not that it turned to the mechanism of causes, but that it saw the world as a mechanism at all – a machine of events. In looking at the events of high tide at Greenwich or an eclipse at the Hague, it looked not at the nature of water or fire, but looked to other events, forward and backward. The Scientific Revolution was a change from a world of things ordered according to their ideal natures, to a world of events running in a steady mechanism of before and after.

CHAPTER 3

Isaac Newton's Model

I

THE great revolutions in outlook are long in the making, and at last they change all our ways of thought. But the change strikes first in one field of knowledge, which has a special place in the social and intellectual life of the day. In the nineteenth century, the field of interest shared by laymen and specialists, in which the new biological sciences first took their stand, was the age of the earth and the descent of man. In the sixteenth and seventeenth centuries the central field of knowledge was astronomy. This was the field of greatest social importance to the trading countries and the trader classes. It was a practical, technical field; but it was not therefore despised as fit only for mariners and mathematicians. Astronomy was a gentleman's accomplishment like singing to the lute, as we see from the number of songs to the lute whose imagery is sprinkled with stars. I have already remarked that Christopher Wren was professor of astronomy, first in London and then in Oxford.

The steps by which there was prepared the great climax and transformation of astronomy in 1687 are now well known, and I will do no more than recall them briefly. Men have known for several thousand years that the sun and the planets move in regular ways against a background of stars which seem to be still. These regularities can be used to look forward as well as back: the Babylonians were able to use them to forecast eclipses of the moon and sun, roughly every eighteen and seventy-six years. The sun, the moon, and the planets can be pictured as being carried round the earth on these regular paths in great shells or spheres. Or the paths, which seen from the earth are curiously looped, can be thought of as the rolling of wheels upon wheels; it was in this way that Ptolemy and other Greeks in Alexandria patterned them on the night sky eighteen hundred years ago. Ptolemy's picture does not claim to explain the movement of the planets, if indeed we could make him understand this meaning of the word 'explain' which has become natural for us. It gives an order to their movements by describing them, and so tells us where we may expect to see them next.

Two things happened in the sixteenth century to make astronomy ill at ease with this description; and they are both of interest, because they remind us that science is compounded of fact and logic. The Danish astronomer Tycho Brahe took better and more regular observations of the positions of the planets, and they showed that Ptolemy's paths, charming though they looked as mathematical curves, were really only rather crude guides to where the planets rolled. And even earlier, in 1543, Copernicus showed that these paths are much simpler if they are looked at not from the earth but from the sun. Early in the seventeenth century, these two findings were combined by Kepler, who had worked for Brahe. Kepler used the measurements of Brahe and the speculations of Copernicus to frame general descriptions of the orbits of the planets: for example, he showed that, seen from the sun as focus, a planet sweeps out equal areas of its ellipse in each equal interval of time.

It was these empirical generalizations of Kepler which Newton and his contemporaries worked from when they began to look for a deeper order below the movements of the planets. They had also a new weapon of theory. For while Kepler had been at work in the north, Galileo in

2

Italy had at last overthrown the physical conceptions in the works of Aristotle, which had long been attacked in Paris. By the time the Royal Society was founded, the complicated Greek ideas of motion with their conflict of earth and air, of impact and vacuum were out of the way. There were no clear new laws of motion yet; it was left to Newton to set these out; but there were fair descriptions of where and how masses in fact move, and no interest at all in where they ought to want to move.

2

What was the nature of Newton's insight? How did he exercise those great gifts, and seize the great opportunity which I have described?

If we put what he did most baldly, it is this: that he carried on the simplification which Kepler had begun, but carried it beyond geometry into physics. Ptolemy, Copernicus, Tycho Brahe, and Kepler at bottom all looked no further than to plot the paths of the planets. Kepler found likenesses between these paths deeper than anything in the traditional astronomy, for his were likenesses of motion as well as shape. Nevertheless his paths remained descriptions, more accurate and more concise than Ptolemy's, but no more universal. For even when Kepler speculated about an attraction of the planets to the sun he had no principle to link it to the movement of earthly masses. Galileo had the first glimpse of that; and there were others as the seventeenth century marched on who knew what kind of principle they were looking for; but it was Newton who formulated it, sudden and entire. He said that change of motion is produced by force; that the motion between masses, whether apple, moon and earth, or planet and sun, is produced by gravitational forces which attract them to one another.

And he alone of his contemporaries had the mathematical power to show that, if these forces are postulated in the right way, then they keep the planets spinning like a clockwork; they keep the moon in her orbit, and the tides moving under the moon; and they hold the universe together. These achievements are so great that they outtop astronomy; and they are only a part of Newton's whole achievement. But more than the achievement, it is the thought within which deserves our study. There is the searching conception of the universe as a machine: not a pattern but a clockwork. There is the conception of the moving forces within the machine: the single spring of action in gravitation. There is the brilliant compromise between the description of the astronomers and the First Cause of the theologians, in which Newton shaped once for all the notion of cause as it has remained ever since. Newton indeed has taken over just enough of the Aristotelean nature of things to make the world work by giving all matter a single nature – that it seeks to join with all other matter. And finally, there is his extraordinary solution of the ambivalence within all science, which is compounded mysteriously of fact and logic, in a way which still remains beyond analysis.

Of these massive achievements I shall single out two. One is Newton's working out of the concept of the cause, by making it over from its scholastic form in, say, St Thomas Aquinas, to the modern form which now seems so obvious to us. This is one theme in this chapter. And I shall go to it by way of a related achievement, and to my mind one which is as remarkable: the marriage of the logical with the empirical method. What Newton did here has equally become a commonplace in scientific method, but one of which we are less aware.

3

In order to act in a scientific manner, in order to act in a human manner at all, two things are necessary: fact and thought. Science does not consist only of finding the facts; nor is it enough only to think, however rationally. The processes of science are characteristic of human action in that they move by the union of empirical fact and rational thought, in a way which cannot be disentangled. There is in science, as in all our lives, a continuous to and fro of actual discovery, then of thought about the implications of what we have discovered, and so back to the facts for testing and discovery – a step by step of experiment and theory, left, right, left, right, for ever.

This union of two methods is the very base of science. Whitehead, who in his philosophy laid stress on it, dated the Scientific Revolution from the moment when Galileo and his contemporaries understood that the two methods, the empirical and the logical, are each meaningless alone, and that they must be put together. In Whitehead's view, the Middle Ages were quite as logical in their speculations about nature as we are. It is not as rationalists that we have the advantage of them; our material successes stem from joining to their logic a ruthless appeal, at each bold deductive step, back to the hard empirical facts. The moment when this was begun, and the authority of the thought and the word was put to the challenge of fact, has long been dramatized in a scene at Pisa. Galileo is said to have dropped a large and a small mass from the Leaning Tower there; and they reached the ground more or less together, in flat contradiction of the pronouncements of Aristotle and Aquinas. But history is rarely so simple or so decisive. Galileo did not make this experiment at Pisa, and those who did could not make it work. And meanwhile logic was already thinking out the experiment. Independent spirits in the bolder school of Paris had for some time doubted Aristotle's dictum that larger masses fall faster. Their logical objection can be put in this way: that since three equal masses dropped together will all fall side by side, it is at least unlikely that two of them should suddenly begin to gain on the third merely because they happen to be tied or formed together into a larger mass.

We need not wonder too nicely whether we shall take this event or that thought as zero hour for the Scientific Revolution. No change of outlook is as direct as Whitehead implies, or as abrupt as I have sometimes dramatically pictured it. The beginnings of the Industrial Revolution go back before 1760, and the beginnings of the Scientific Revolution go back long before 1660 or indeed that earlier day, real or fabled, on the Leaning Tower of Pisa about 1590. But our concern is not with beginnings; it is with the visible substantial change, from the outlook before to the outlook after. The outlook before the Scientific Revolution was content with scholastic logic applied to a nature of hierarchies. The Scientific Revolution ended that: it linked the rational and the empirical, thought and fact, theory and practical experiment. And this has remained the content of science ever since. From time to time great speculative scientists like Eddington have seemed to claim again that we can deduce all physical laws without any experiments. But when we study their work, we find that it is not at all a return to the Middle Ages; and that their real claim is that the physical laws can be deduced from far fewer critical experiments than we have been in the habit of thinking necessary.

4

Two great thinkers in the first half of the seventeenth century are usually coupled, the one with the rational and the other with the empirical approach in science. The method of logic is given to Descartes, and the method of experiment to Francis Bacon. And the two men do indeed form a nice contrast between what are usually held to be the French and the English habits of thought. Characteristically, Descartes did most of his scientific work in bed; and Bacon died of a cold which he caught, says Thomas Hobbes, when at the age of sixty-five he tried the experiment of stuffing a fowl with snow. Certainly the powerful influence of Descartes tended to run counter to the inquisitive English school, more perhaps because of its rigidity of form than its content. I have remarked that Huygens had been influenced by Descartes, whom he knew well as a boy; and this was one of the things which kept Huygens from understanding the full range of what Newton and the Royal Society were doing.

But the example of Descartes was as essential to Newton's frame of mind as was Bacon's. In some ways indeed it was more important. For the Royal Society was full of tireless experimenters in the grand and somewhat haphazard manner of Bacon. What it lacked was Descartes's search for system, his belief that nature is always and everywhere alike and a unity, which to him and Newton was symbolized by the universal power of mathematics. Descartes's whole life was shaped by a moment of insight in which suddenly, late one night, it was revealed to him with an immediacy which was almost physical, that the key to the universe is its mathematical order. To the end of his life, Descartes remembered the date of that revelation, 10 November 1619 – he was then twenty-three – and he always spoke of it with the awe of a mystic. By contrast, Bacon altogether underrated the importance of the mathematical method, and here his influence was bad.

I have said that the empirical and the logical methods in science must take alternate steps forward; a step in one makes ready for a step in the other. It is natural that the empirical method should stress the facts, and should ask the theoretically minded thinker to make his deductions from them. It is as natural that the thinker should construct a world and then look up to see how far in fact it is the world of fact. Most of us today have a strong bias for the empirical. As laymen we feel that the facts are wonderful and the theory is always difficult; and we tend to think of all science as a logical process taking the facts and deducing from them some system which they determine. This is not what Newton did, nor indeed, surprising as it may seem, is it the usual method of science as we know it. On the contrary, what is surprising is that we should believe this deductive method to be practised or practicable.

What Newton did was something quite different. He took from the experiments of Galileo and other Italians some general notions about how masses behave: that they travel in straight lines and at a uniform pace, that they go on travelling so unless a force displaces them, and so on. So far, the method may be called deductive, because it rests fairly closely on experiment; although even here deduction does not give quite the right picture of the method, which calls for a great deal of mental experiment in building up possible worlds from different laws.

But it is at the next step that the break really comes. What Newton did now was to suppose that the general rules which fair-sized masses seem to obey are true of every piece of matter, whatever its kind or its size. And having decided to try this thought, he made himself a new world of his own, which he built up from minute pieces of matter each following the same laws or axioms. This world is just as much a construction as the abstract world of geometry which Euclid built up out of his axioms. Euclid defined a point, a line, a plane, and he laid down axioms which these are to obey in their mutual relations. He then constructed in a series of propositions a large number of consequences which flow from these. And what makes us honour Euclid is that this abstract world now turns out to be recognizably like that part of the real world which we can see and compare with our own eyes. We believe in his axioms, not because they are deduced from the real world, but because the consequences which he constructs from them fit the real world.

This was very much Newton's method too, but Newton almost for the first time applied it to the physical world. He supposed that everything in the world is assembled from small particles. He never defined these particles, and we have come to think of them as the atoms of Democritus and the poet Lucretius. Newton did not say this, and I am not sure that he believed it; I am not sure that he really wanted to get into arguments, whether these particles really could not be cut up into smaller ones. Although he wrote with great clarity, Newton was not good in argument and he tried to avoid it. This was not because Newton could not see his opponent's difficulty, but because he had foreseen and resolved it in his own work so long ago that he despaired of helping any one who could not work round it alone. As a result, Newton was a difficult and morose man in his relations with other scientists, and was not so much impatient as hopeless about persuading any one who could not himself think through the natural but removable obstacles.

Newton then built up his world of unknown small

particles assembled in such masses as the apple, the moon, the planets, and the sun. Each of these assemblies is alike in his view in being made up of these minute pieces of matter. And in each of them the minute pieces obey the same laws; if they are at rest then they remain at rest, or if they are moving they go on moving steadily in straight lines, until they are displaced by outside forces. Greatest among these forces is this, that each minute particle in Newton's world attracts every other equal particle with a force which depends only on their distance apart, falling off in such a way that when the distance is doubled, the force shrinks to a quarter.

Now this is of course a fictitious world. It is a picture, and so far it has not even been shown to be a machine. That is, we do not even know at this stage whether it will go on doing whatever we started it doing. It might simply not work, either because all its particles would fly apart for ever, or because they would all collapse into the centre. So far in fact we have only the definitions and the axioms: the next step is, as in Euclid, to work out the propositions, that is the consequences of this shadow dance among the ghostly particles. And this is where Newton showed his power as a mathematician. Hooke and others who had already guessed at much the same picture got no further than general speculation because they lacked the mathematical skill to work out the exact consequences. First, it is necessary to show that under these laws an assembly of particles which form a compact sphere behaves towards anything outside the sphere simply like one heavy particle at its centre. The simplicity of the mathematics, which makes astronomy manageable, depends critically on this fact; and this fact in turn depends on a gravitation which falls off as the square of the distance and not in some other way. In a world with another law of gravitation, though it might differ only minutely from the law of inverse squares, round heavenly bodies would not act like single points of concentrated matter, and in general the planetary paths would be neither calculable nor stable.

And this is only the first step. Newton went on to show that as a result of this the orbits of the planets can be calculated; that they are the ellipses which Kepler had measured; and that they remain stable paths turning like a divine clockwork. He went on to calculate the tides and the paths of comets; and so he slowly built up a picture of the world which is recognizably the world as the mariner sees it, and the astronomer, and the picnickers on Brighton beach. The world of speculation is suddenly seen to chime with the real world, with a triumphant note like a peal of bells.

It is this accord which makes us believe in Newton's picture, and underneath it in his laws. The laws are not a deduction from experiment in any obvious sense. Their success is not that they follow from the real world, but that they predict a world which is essentially like ours. And it is this success which gives us our faith in the substratum of tiny particles each obeying the laws on which Newton's picture is built. This assumption under the picture, this faith in a minute substratum has had important consequences in shaping our methods and our metaphysics ever since; and we shall have occasion to turn to it again.

5

In describing Newton's reconstruction of the starry world, I have likened it to Euclid's manner of building up something recognizably like the space round us from a set of hypothetical entities which are assumed to obey a few simple rules. Where Newton's achievement differs from Euclid's is in this: what is constructed is required to fit the observed facts more closely and in greater variety. I am tempted to say that the physical facts are also more immediate and more important than the facts of geometry. But I am not sure that this is not an illusion which we all have because Euclid's work has been part of civilized thinking for more than two thousand years, whereas Newton's, although now three hundred years old, still inspires in us something of the astonishing sense of destiny in simplicity which it had for his contemporaries. In fact, the fit of Euclid's geometrical construction to our space lies snugly under the physical fit of Newton's picture. But there is a difference. Newton's physics fits at more points, and had to be checked and enlarged to fit there in his time and throughout the eighteenth and nineteenth centuries. It has to meet more detailed and powerful experimental tests, because it is a construction which claims to fit from moment to moment a world in constant changing movement. This is what makes it more difficult and deeper than Euclid's reconstruction of the timeless, windless world of space.

And this is why I called Newton's method the joining of the two strands in science, the rational and the empirical. Here the logical outlook of Descartes is joined with the experimental passion of Bacon; and it is right to recall again how able and how searching an experimenter Newton himself was. The *Principia* gives us a wonderful sense of his intellectual power, because the experimental work on which it rested at that stage had been done by others and was familiar. But the *Opticks* is as impressive a book with a more personal immediacy, because in it he takes us from one experiment to the next with such clarity and such insight that more than anything we are silenced by the roundness and coherence of his method. We have the sense here that nothing that matters has been left untested, and yet there is no random pottering about just to see if there might be anything in this or that as well. Newton had that insight which cannot be distracted, that gift for isolating and eliminating each logical alternative, which makes the profound experimental as well as the theoretical scientist: which makes of course simply the profound mind.

We do not see the young man of the *Opticks* in the measured pages of the *Principia*, though even when the *Principia* was printed, long after Newton had done the work in it, he was still in his forties. But the power is the same: to construct hypothetical parts and assemble them into a mechanism which shall fit at each stage the experimental checks and the real world; and at the same time to invent as in the *Opticks* or to identify as in the *Principia* the critical checks at the right points. That is why I underline the union of thought and fact, the rational and the empirical streams flowing together. The Scientific Revolution was the point of their confluence, and the power of the scientific method since then has derived, like the power of the Rhône, from two streams rolled into one.

6

The other great step which was taken at the Scientific Revolution was in giving a new and clear meaning to the concept of cause. There is a great deal of argument about causes in the scholastic writers of the Middle Ages. Aquinas has a formidable array of their categories – proximate causes, efficient causes, necessary causes, and the First Cause. And under these concepts runs the medieval notion that every part of nature is endowed with a human will and temper, and strives to a purpose of its own. These causes are all trappings of logic; but the notion of cause and effect as the sixteenth and seventeenth centuries slowly worked it out is not one of logical consequence. In the nineteenth century, philosophers tried with great pains to recover some logical, that is mental, necessity in the sequence of cause and effect: John Stuart Mill's is the outstanding effort. But this really is to try once again to inject into the physical world the workings of the human mind. It is a sort of pathetic fallacy of science, like that pathetic fallacy of poetry which makes nature weep with Milton for the death of Lycidas.

The notion of cause which since the Scientific Revolution is so natural and obvious to us is not the notion of a logical sequence. Like other great principles of science, such as the principles that nature is rational and is uniform, its sanction is metaphysical. In effect this means that it is a working rule based on our experience of the past and on the way that we organize our lives on that experience in order to meet the future. Our conception of cause and effect is this: that given a definite configuration of wholly material things, there will always follow upon it the same observable event. If we repeat the configuration, we shall always get the same event following it. As the sun sets, radio reception improves. As we press the switch, the light goes on. As the child grows, it becomes able to speak. And if the expected does not happen, if reception does not improve or the lamp does not light up, or the child persists in gurgling, then we are confident that the configuration from which we started was not the same. There has been something misplaced, we are sure, and this something is material and has injected a material difference into the assumed configuration, which has worked everywhere else and at all other times. The present influences the future and, more, it determines it.

This is the concept of cause which has been elevated to the rank of the central concept of science. And it did in fact play a major part in clarifying what was new at the Scientific Revolution, and made Newton's world different from that of Aristotle. When the world became a machine, this became the god within the machine. But I shall show that its importance has been overrated. There are two other changes which to my mind are more important. One is the change from the world of will to the world of machine. The other is the change on which I have laid greatest stress, from a world of hierarchies to the modelled world of Newton which is built upon a substratum of undefined particles and simple laws, yet which clocks in triumphantly at each revolution upon the orbits of the real world. The notion of cause is an essential cement within both these, within the machine and within the model. But it is not the fundamental notion. It can be replaced by other cements. And if it is not replaced at the right time, it can bring the machine and the model themselves to a standstill. This has been so historically and is apparent in the problems in science and outside it today. This is what I now turn to, in history and in the present.

CHAPTER 4

The Eighteenth Century and the Idea of Order

I

NEWTON'S great work was over before the eighteenth century began. He became Master of the Mint in 1699. He directed its work with energy and care, and it was because he approved Wood's halfpence in the 1720s that Swift made a special butt of him. But he made no more bold speculations except on such topics as the meaning of the Book of Revelation. And since he had eccentric views on religion, he did himself no good with these at Cambridge. He was knighted but he never held a college office.

I have taken Newton's achievement for a compact symbol of the whole Scientific Revolution. I take his loss of interest equally as a convenient symbol for the decay of science in the eighteenth century. There was a loss of power and invention, a thickening and a dulling of the fine edge of promise, which is as astonishing as the promise itself had been. The great climax of the 1660s, like the bursting of a dam, was only just past. The Royal Society and the Académie Royale des Sciences had been founded. Men like Huygens, the Bernoullis, Fontenelle, scientists and popularizers, artists and writers had crowded to share the new interests and the new skills. There never had been such a blaze of promise; and it lasted to the turn of the century. Let me quote a last example. About 1700, two of the leading architects in England were Christopher Wren and John Vanbrugh. The one was finishing St Paul's, and the other was beginning Blenheim. But I have already remarked that Wren was also a distinguished mathematician; and Vanbrugh had just written *The Relapse*, which is at least one of the livelier among the mechanical comedies of the Restoration.

No one could have foreseen at that moment that Augustan literature and science would soon decline both to a level dullness. Philosophy grew smug and sceptical together, in the minor thinkers like Bolingbroke and in greater men too, in Berkeley and Hume. The eighteenth-century manner became a tolerant, comfortable, but at bottom a deeply cynical reverence for ancient institutions. It is Gibbon's manner to the Roman Empire, and is the special charm of Boswell's manner to Dr Johnson.

This is not a helpful manner, and it is particularly discouraging to science, which is essentially inquisitive, inventive, and rather earnest. Of course it is natural that Swift in *Gulliver's Travels* should treat science as one of the funnier frauds of the South Sea Bubble. It is natural that Pope and Gay sneered at the collectors and fossil hunters.

> *Philosophers more grave than wise*
> *Hunt science down in Butterflies;*
> *Or fondly poring on a Spider,*
> *Stretch human contemplation wider;*
> Fossiles *give joy to* Galen's *soul,*
> *He digs for knowledge, like a Mole;*
> *In shells so learn'd, that all agree*
> *No fish that swims knows more than he!*
> *In such pursuits if wisdom lies,*
> Who, Laura, *shall thy taste despise?*

They were the defeated Tories, and it was natural that they should be bitter about the success of scientists, most of whom were dissenters and Whigs. The Royal Society had not been able altogether to ignore the scientific member of their Scriblerus set, Dr Arbuthnot, physician to Queen Anne, mathematician, satirist, and creator of John Bull. Nevertheless the Society under Newton's presidency for twenty-five years now became, like Augustan society, something of a Whig preserve.

The Tory grumbles about science and scholarship are therefore understandable; they were grumbling at the Whigs. But the Whig intellects from Addison and Steele onwards gave science as little honour. The great men of either party were no longer interested in the Royal Society, as Cowley and Waller and Dryden had been. And as the eighteenth century hardened into convention, the Society became a club for peers and dilettanti, in which for a hundred years the scientists formed a cowed and servile minority.

As a result, the real science of the eighteenth century was practised by social oddities: by eccentrics like Cavendish or the Oxford antiquaries, by Unitarians and Quakers from the Midlands, and by untaught mechanics like James Brindley who designed the whole system of English waterways but never learned to spell 'navigation'. The century settled down in two camps of Philistines: the literary Philistines and, largely to spite them, the scientific Philistines. It was the beginning of the mistaken opposition between them from which we still suffer.

2

What were the reasons for this unexpected reversal? There were at least three. First, England in the seventeenth century had been a seafaring nation, and like Holland was therefore dominated by the sciences of navigation: astronomy, hydraulics, optics, and the design of clocks. Charles II founded the observatory at Greenwich within a few years of the Royal Society. But had England remained a seafaring nation, she would have decayed in the eighteenth century just as Holland did. What made England then expand immensely beyond her marine greatness was that she was also a manufacturing nation. She outstripped Holland and France in the conquest of the world because she had wool and iron and coal, and with them the means to use cotton. The Royal Society had not been ignorant of this. Its earlier meetings had laid stress on the study of practical matters: dyeing and coining, gunnery and refining, the diving bell and the statistics of population. But though it was in the power of the Society to see these needs, it was not in its power to satisfy them. The new sciences had to be created by men at home in their crafts: simple, practical, and not at all respectable men. It would have needed a very energetic society to have recruited such men in the eighteenth century, and to break down the social obstacles to their entry. Given the choice, the respectable Royal Society naturally and helplessly fell to the lordlings.

The second misfortune of science was precisely the spectacular success of Newton's system in astronomy. The sweep and finality of his system, which like the Goddess of Wisdom seemed to his contemporaries to step fully formed from a single brain, was a visible example. From a puzzle of loose observations and working rules he had produced a single system ordered only by mathematics and a few axioms: ordered, it seemed, by a single divine edict, the law of inverse squares. Here was the traditional problem of the trader nations since Bible times; its solution meant something to every educated man. And its solution was so remarkably simple: everyone could grasp the law of inverse squares. From the moment that it was seen that this lightning flash of clarity was sufficient –

> *God said*, Let Newton be ! *and All was* Light

– from this moment it was felt that here plainly was the order of God. And plainly therefore the mathematical method was the method of nature, a model for all scientific orders. The *Principia* had been published only five years when Dr Bentley, the famous classical scholar and tyrant of Trinity, asked and got Newton's consent to lecture on the laws of gravitation as the final example of God's design. The result was that what had been a living discovery hardened quickly into a rigid prison of system. To eighteenth-century thinkers, at least in England, the universe was settled once for all. Any new idea, say the idea of energy, could not grow in it; it had to enter at last from outside. It is characteristic that Newton's work in astronomy was enlarged and rounded in the eighteenth century not in England but in France, where Voltaire had taken it as a system without a God. Even Newton's mathematical invention of the calculus stood still in England while every mathematician on the continent, taking it from Leibnitz, was driving ahead with it.

3

This brings me to the third failing of eighteenth-century science, which I find the most interesting. A science which orders its thought too early is stifled. For example, the ideas of the Epicureans about atoms two thousand years ago were quite reasonable; but they did only harm to a physics which could not yet measure temperature and pressure and learn the simpler laws which relate them. Or again, the hope of the medieval alchemists that the elements might be changed was not as fanciful as we once thought. But it was merely damaging to a chemistry which did not yet understand the composition of water and common salt.

The ambition of the eighteenth-century systematizers was to impose a mathematical finality on history and biology and geology and mining and spinning. It was a mistaken ambition and very damaging. A science is a description of the world or, better, a language for describing the world. When a science has been studied as long as astronomy, it can develop a concise description in the shorthand of laws like Newton's. But before this can happen it must have the observations not only of Tycho Brahe and Kepler, but of the Moors and the Greeks and even the Babylonians. Until a science has passed through a long stage of observation and trial, it cannot develop a system of ordering its observations; and it is mere presumption to try to fit it with so ambitious an order as Newton's.

Indeed there is no reason to think that the mathematical method is even appropriate to every science. But we need not stay to argue that in this context. What is certain here is that, even where the method of axioms ruling a substratum of elementary particles or events is appropriate, it simply cannot be applied until that science has an exceptionally full record of observations. In the eighteenth century, there was no science with an orderly history of observations except astronomy. There was in fact at the time no further scope for the mathematical method at all.

Therefore the important progress in science in the eighteenth century was made not under the domination of the mathematicians, but out of sight by two kinds of empirical workers. There were the self-made inventors of whom I have already spoken, like Brindley and the Wedgwoods and the Darby family and James Watt. And there were the observers and collectors, the eccentric virtuosi, of whom it was fashionable to make fun. They were men like Sir Hans Sloane, whose collection began the British Museum, and simple observers of the country-side like Gilbert White of Selborne. They were travellers coming back with antiques from Italy and inscriptions from Turkey. Thomas Jefferson, the American statesman, is the model of the scientific observer and collector of the age. He collected everything from flints to Indian languages, and observed everything from American plants to the French Revolution; and he was at the same time a great humanist.

In England, this temper and that of the industrial inventor were combined in the little societies run by go-ahead manufacturers in the Midlands and the north. Such societies were the Manchester Literary and Philosophical Society, which encouraged the chemist Dalton, and the Lunar Society of Birmingham, where men like Joseph Priestley and Josiah Wedgwood and probably Wilkinson and Edgeworth met. Erasmus Darwin, the grandfather of Charles Darwin, was a member of the Lunar Society. His botanical primers in verse, taking such subjects as *The Loves of the Plants*, brought the new approach into the rigid teaching of the time.

4

The best example of the new order which was being discovered in the non-mathematical sciences is botany. It remains to this day the creation of a number of observers, among them the Swedish naturalist Linnaeus, who set out in the eighteenth century the system of classification by species and families on which it still rests. What kind of order was Linnaeus looking for? Why did his order seem so plainly more reasonable than, say, a grading of flowers by their colours?

This is the most difficult question in science. The notion of order cannot be defined on any ground except its success. It cannot be put into a science in advance at all. It is not obviously silly to classify flowers by their colours; after all, the bluer flowers do tend to be associated with colder climates and greater heights. There is nothing wrong with the system, in advance. It simply does not work as conveniently and as instructively as Linnaeus's classification by family likenesses.

Order is the selection of one set of appearances rather than another because it gives a better sense of the reality behind the appearances. Science is an orderly language for describing some events and predicting others like them. The order is a selection of appearances. And any selection itself implies, and imposes, an interpretation. If we choose a successful order, as Linnaeus and his contemporaries did, we lead that science naturally to the discovery first of evolution and ultimately of the way that inheritance works. If we choose a far-sighted arrangement of the chemical elements in order, as the periodic table does, it leads us by steps to the theories both of molecules and of atomic structure. In each case, our choice has been an unconscious interpretation; just as the literary realist interprets life by the very act of choosing the slice of it which he holds out so faithfully and so depressingly.

We have a great deal to learn from these unassuming orders of the eighteenth-century naturalists. Their odd minds were remarkably free from theoretical prejudices; they had to be, to resist the prestige of the mathematical method. And they made the language of their science in the most human way, like the making of a character. We cannot change our character, we can only enlarge it. If we are wise, then we go on learning all through life, and go on fitting what is new to what we have learned before, piece by piece. And at the end of our life we have a full and orderly personality in which the boy, the undergraduate, the fanatic, and the lover all remain and are all enlarged and fulfilled. It is the collector's and the biologist's and the historian's order: the sort of order which fills Frazer's *Golden Bough*, say, with the sense of real people busy with customs which they really enjoy. It is an order which other scientists and humanists might envy.

5

This is the important step in every science: the construction of a first order which is reasonable in itself and which holds to the experimental facts that are known. We see it with the greatest clarity in the order which Linnaeus and others brought to botany, which had such far-reaching effects later in evolution and then in genetics. But it was equally important in the other sciences which in the eighteenth century still had no orderly body of observations, though some of them were of great age. The obvious examples are the other biological sciences. Think of the most important of them, medicine. It is as old as recorded history; and even earlier, operations like repanning were known to prehistoric man. It had a high standing at least since Greek times. It attracted some of the best medieval and Renaissance minds, particularly among the Moors and Jews of North Africa and Spain. Great discoveries had been made in it in the seventeenth century, for example by William Harvey about the function and power of the heart as a pump. And medicine certainly did not lack a system. Words which we still use, like 'phlegmatic' and 'fiery', witness the long and lasting influence of its system of four humours. For the theory of the humours was not only the theory of psychological types which Ben Jonson's plays have made familiar to us. It was a theory of medical types, founded in turn on the theory of the four elements which I sketched earlier.

The theory of humours tried to analyse diseases and temperaments into one or more of four extreme types: earthy, watery, airy, or fiery. The folly of the theory was that it tried to impose a system on events which had not been sufficiently observed; and in time it came to shape the observations themselves by the system. In the eighteenth century the doctors dominated by it could think of no advances except to reduce their observations to fewer extremes than the classical four. Let me take the example of one man, not because it is out of the way, but because he was a man of forceful manner and fighting temper who stated his notions more roundly than his cautious colleagues. This forceful character was Dr John Brown of Edinburgh, who was something of a stormy petrel of medicine, but was also one of its distinguished leaders and a man who made real contributions in diagnosis and in technique. About 1780 Dr John Brown laid it down that all diseases have one of two causes. They are due either to the tenseness of the solid parts of the body, or to their laxness. There are therefore only two treatments: a soporific for tenseness and a stimulant for laxness. The soporific recommended by Dr John Brown was laudanum and the stimulant was whisky.

It was these large reckless theories which made a caricature of medicine and turned the doctor into a quack: bleeding, drugging and sawing, curing Bishop Berkeley with tar-water and killing Oliver Goldsmith with fever powders, all by rules which were simply fanciful. The great advances in medicine from the end of the eighteenth century were of quite a different kind. They were scrupulous observations of the complex of symptoms which characterizes one disease and not another. Doctors at last defined a disease and distinguished it; they stopped calling it fever and recognized it as typhus or malaria or influenza. This modest practical approach gave a meaning to diagnosis and then to experiment and specific cure. It was typical of the best work of the century, a patient work of observation and order which was not to be diverted by the triumphs of astronomy. We can see it at work in the steps by which smallpox and cowpox were shown to be related, and a preventative treatment was worked out, first by infection and then by inoculation – from Lady Mary Wortley Montagu at the beginning of the eighteenth century to Dr Jenner at the end, in 1796.

This pioneer work was given unity and fulfilment in the nineteenth century. The geologists and the fossil-hunters had been tapping away for a hundred years before they pieced together the single story of the earth's crust. The story astonished and alarmed the religious world of the early nineteenth century. Fifty years later the careful botanical and animal observations fell into place as suddenly and as uncomfortably. Linnaeus had classified these observations by what I have loosely called family likenesses. Now Darwin gave ground for the view that they were literally *family* likenesses; the creatures have them in common because they have a common ancestry – they come from the same family. The likenesses were no longer merely a method of classification; they were suddenly seen as the living footprints of their historic causes.

There was a similar enlargement in time in the other experimental sciences, physical as well as biological. In the eighteenth century, physics, chemistry, electricity, engineering were not ready for systems, and this was one reason why they had no social standing. The manufacturer and the mechanic were their own experimenters, and their restless interest created industrial England and

the new sciences together. Think for a moment of the
firm of Boulton and Watt making steam engines in
Birmingham. From the 1780s both partners were leaders
among English men of science, and were even able to
crash into the Royal Society in spite of their radical sympathies. More, they were able to put into the Society a
third man, William Murdock, who had come to the firm
as a workman wearing a wooden hat which he had
turned on a lathe to show what a skilled man could do
with his hands. These were the men who made the physical sciences over, in the Lunar Society and the Mechanics' Institutes and all the little clubs of dissenting
men of skill and spirit.

Once again, what is familiar today is what the nineteenth century made of their experimental work, round-
ing it and unifying it into a single order. Dalton showed
the physical basis of chemical behaviour, and Humphry
Davy its electrical basis. Faraday found the link between mechanical movement and electric current. By
the middle of the nineteenth century there was a general
belief that all forms of energy are at bottom identical.
About 1860 Clerk Maxwell gave mathematical form to
this belief; and did for physics much what Newton had
done for astronomy two hundred years before. Another
settled, rational optimism like that of the age of Walpole
seemed about to descend on Queen Victoria's England.

6

The time of which I have been speaking, the century and
a half roughly from 1730 to 1880, is one of the most
violent in the world's history. Frederick the Great began
the expansion of Prussia, the elder Pitt took Canada and
India from the French, the United States of America
were created in two wars; the French Revolution and

wars made Europe over and over; reform and reaction, Chartism, revolution, and repression ebbed to and fro; and the period ends with the rise of the German empire and industry. And below these political changes are changes as great in the lives and preoccupations of their societies. Europe changed from a loose jumble of agricultural countries to the harsh rivalry of states, in each of which industry was shaping the forms of life and government. In England this period was dominated by the Industrial Revolution. By the time the Prince Consort opened the Great Exhibition in the Crystal Palace in Hyde Park in 1851, there was almost nothing there which could have been seen or even thought of at Strawberry Hill when Horace Walpole was settling in a hundred years earlier. In those hundred years the population of England had risen from six to eighteen millions. The scattered villages where handworkers and their children made cloth and nails and beaver hats in the West Riding and the Midlands had grown into the industrial towns of Leeds and Sheffield and Manchester and Birmingham and Liverpool. Coal, iron, and cotton had become the backbone of England, whose staple before had been wool and open-field farming.

The inventions which changed England in the late eighteenth century were cast iron made with coal, the steam engine, the spinning mule, the power loom, and the factory system. These and the agricultural advances which were made at the same time were technical discoveries. To some extent therefore they were based on the scientific discoveries of the seventeenth century. But the extent is not large: there is little in Arkwright's spinning frame or even in the steam engine which Leonardo da Vinci would not have understood. No, the important effect of the Scientific Revolution had been, not in discovering the means for these machines, but in preparing

the climate for them. What had happened since 1660
had been that the interest in such devices had become
widespread. Hargreaves who invented the jenny was a
weaver, Cartwright was a parson when he invented the
power loom, and the canal-minded Duke of Bridgewater
was a coal-owner. These men differed from others like
them a hundred years earlier less in knowledge and in-
genuity than in temper. It was natural for them to think
of the mechanics of industry and of its finance. Arkwright
who was a barber and something of a rolling stone really
had no other insight than what we should call industrial
management. He saw the factory itself as a machine,
and industry as a kind of mint.

These changes took place so quickly and in so many
fields that I have not tried to follow them here. Nor do I
want to search for their first causes; it has never been
clear how the Industrial Revolution developed its great
speed and scale. Our interest is in the relation of the
Industrial Revolution to the concepts of science. Science
did not bring about the Industrial Revolution. It did not
even precipitate it, for science was quite out of touch with
such work in the eighteenth century; and knew nothing
that could help John Roebuck to make sulphuric acid in
Edinburgh or Benjamin Franklin to fly a kite in a thun-
derstorm, or that most inspired of American adventurers
Count Rumford to bore cannon in Munich. What
science did for these men, and for thousands like them in
mines, at mills, and in workshops, was to set their interests
free. They no longer thought of the world either as settled
or as well taken care of. They saw the world as man-made
and ordered by man, and they saw the machine in every
part of it. This is striking even in the imagination of the
mystics of the Industrial Revolution. Swedenborg's writ-
ings remind us that he had been an expert on metals and
mines, and Blake's prophetic books are crowded with the

symbolism of wheels turning on wheels, the good wheels with the sun and the evil ones against it. It had always been a favourite fancy among Pythagoreans and Cabbalists and those who read the future in the Pyramids, to relate events and names to numbers. But it was left characteristically to Watt's hard-headed business partner Boulton to draw a mystic sense of mission from the year of his birth, which was 1728, because that is the number of cubic inches in a cubic foot.

CHAPTER 5

The Nineteenth Century and the Idea of Causes

I

I AM nearing the central problems in scientific method today: and I want to spare no pains to make clear what is at issue there. In many scientific problems, the difficulty is to state the question rightly; once that is done, it may almost answer itself. This is at least as true of philosophical problems. It is true above all of problems of method, which trouble us now.

That is why I want to be sure that we never lose sight of the steps by which science has come to suppose that all laws must be framed in causal form. These steps form an important sequence, and the dominance of the causal laws comes only at their end. We must not take it for granted that science is necessarily and is only the search for laws of cause and effect.

Science begins with the belief that the world is orderly: or better, that it can be made orderly by human arrangement. This arrangement consists of putting things in groups, not of identical things, but of things which seem to be or behave alike. I say behave alike because the activity of ordering is not carried out, as Adam is said to have named the creatures, merely by sitting still and calling out likely words. It is an experimental activity of trial and error. We must from the outset underline its empirical nature, because there is no test for what is like and what is unlike except an empirical one: that the arrangement of things in these groups chimes and fits with the kind of world, the kind of life which we act out.

In particular, we judge things to be like in important ways and not in others before we set up a group into which we throw them together. We judge it to be more important, that is more helpful and more searching, to make one group of the mammals than of creatures which swim or which lay eggs; and this even when it creates anomalies like the whale and the duck-billed platypus. We order by likenesses, and we choose those likenesses which we first judge and then find to have significance.

Next, it is a tenet of science that the processes which it studies are machines. This does not mean that their action must resemble that of some imaginary construct assembled from levers, pulleys, springs, magnets, dynamos, and radio valves. No such construct was able to ape the behaviour of the ether in the physics of Clerk Maxwell; but it was not for this reason that the ether was abandoned. It was abandoned because it turned out to have no properties which might not just as well be written into the brief for space. And no such mechanical construct can reproduce the properties of space as we imagine it today; yet we do not suppose that space is otherwise than mechanical. A machine in science is a concept with definite properties which can be isolated, can be reproduced in space and in time, and whose behaviour can be predicted. And we do not mean by this that its behaviour is determined in every particular. The laws of inheritance as they were formulated by Mendel make a machine, although they do not claim to forecast the colour of each grandchild when pink and white garden peas are crossed. They make a machine even though they specifically include random couplings among the genes. There is nothing in our concept of a machine to exclude from it a choice made by tossing a penny or looking up a table of random numbers, or forecasting the future in a form which says that tomorrow will be fine three times out of ten. And of course the modification of inheritance which Lamarck suggested at the end of the eighteenth century is equally a machine. For it also postulates that the biological process can be isolated from the arbitrary irruption of unknown factors, and can be reduced to a law-abiding sequence of operations by named agents.

The machine repeats; the model mimics. The postulate of the machine is that from the same beginnings will follow the same ends. There need not be only one end, but if there are more then they must occur in repeatable proportions over repeated trials. The model sets up behind the machine a hypothetical world which yields the same ends. In the model, the steps by which these ends are reached from these beginnings are exhibited. That is, the model defines a set of fundamental units, and states laws or axioms which they are to obey; and it shows that, if the real world were in fact made up from these units, obeying these laws, then its behaviour would coincide with what we observe. In the illustration which I took from Mendel, the machine simply says that the self-crossing of the offspring of white and pink garden peas yields a new generation of whites and pinks in nearly constant proportion; and therefore empirically we can foretell or test the proportion, one to three. The model postulates a way, not by which nature reaches this proportion, but by which it might reach it. For this purpose, it postulates the genes and their laws of random assortment. Of course, the model as much as the machine is free to include links of random choices. A model does not need to be driven by the springs of cause and effect.

2

Nevertheless, the idea of cause and effect has taken powerful hold on our minds. We have the greatest difficulty in freeing ourselves from its compulsion, even when we are thinking through scientific problems with conscious care. And unconsciously, we fall back on it at every turn. This has become our natural way of looking at all problems.

The reason is to be found in the success which Victorian scientists had when they took cause and effect as their guiding principle. I have written at length of the failure of the formal sciences in the eighteenth century to advance either biology or the new experimental work in physics, chemistry, electricity, and magnetism. In the eighteenth century what these sciences needed was observation and experiment. But the nineteenth century was able to build on that spade work, and to unify it into the great body of the biological and physical sciences as it stood at the beginning of our century.

Unity had been created in each of these fields of knowledge by bringing into it the orderly working of cause and effect. This idea came to dominate the Victorians. It became the centre of scientific method for them, as it had been for Newton's contemporaries from whom of course they derived it. What had so impressed those contemporaries in their time, and had hamstrung them in every other scientific field, had been Newton's success in putting causes into the night sky. The planets are caused to keep their orbits, Newton had said, by a kind of invisible celestial elastic: the force of gravitation. And by Jupiter, that simple model of causes worked!

Now the nineteenth century was heartened by successes of the same kind, above all in physics, until it came to demand a mechanism of cause and effect in every science. The point is illustrated by the difference between the discoveries in geology and in biology at which I have glanced. At the beginning of the century, geology had not hesitated to challenge the Bible story of the Creation, without offering any very precise chain of cause and effect in its place. The evidence of the rocks was thought to be sufficient. When believers objected that God might after all Himself have interleaved the strata and put in the fossils, the geologists did not think it necessary to prove this impractical; they were content to consider it perverse. That simply was not their idea of how a rational world is run. Their view of nature was that which Einstein has since fixed in the remark that God is ingenious but He is not malicious.

But the biologists later on were more cautious. Most of them believed that there has been evolution: that is, that species owe their likeness to common descent. But none of them was willing to commit himself to the belief, until he knew some mechanism of cause and effect which might have produced the differences and the likenesses. Charles Darwin did not invent the theory of evolution; that was known to his grandfather. What he thought of was a machinery for evolution: the mechanism of natural selection. Darwin saw that evolution is explained if we assume that the environment causes better adapted animals to survive in the competition with their rivals – the struggle for existence. Once Darwin had proposed this chain of cause and effect, the theory of evolution was accepted by every one; and it was thought the most natural thing in the world to call it Darwin's theory.

After two hundred years then, Newton's method, the method of causes and mechanisms, had become the standard method for every science. No other method was conceivable; any other order was thought merely a stop-gap. And there were many sciences, like those I have been describing, where this insistence on a causal system did have admirable results. But there have been others where the results have been disastrous. Look for example at economics. It has never become an empirical science because it has never recovered from the fatal reasonableness of Adam Smith's *Wealth of Nations*. Look at psychology. In psychology, the word *cause* has been translated as motive or compulsion, and the word *effect* has been translated as behaviour. And the mechanical systems which have been built on this are really no improvement on the old theory of humours.

This example is not irrelevant. We are all much concerned with the relation of motives to behaviour. Our literature has been concerned with little else since the Romantic Revival. But no sensitive observer can be content with the kind of crude analysis of motives which still passes for scientific. Writers have therefore felt themselves to be writing against the stream of scientific beliefs. They have pictured themselves and their heroes as eccentrics or rebels – as souls lost or at bay in a closing world. This has given them the air of pessimism which has hung over the novel from Thomas Hardy to Virginia Woolf.

3

We are here facing the liveliest and the deepest problem which nature has put to us since the Scientific Revolution. And what gives it its sharp point and charm is that it is not merely a technical problem in scientific method. It is a problem in a corner of metaphysics about which we are all able to think and free to speak; at least, we are free to speak if we are willing to think. A difficulty of lay discussion on scientific subjects is usually this, that there exists no common language in which scientists and laymen can talk together about scientific ideas. In each generation, the subjects which blaze into the headlines are therefore those rare exceptions where such a language does happen to exist. This is why the nineteenth century got so excited about the age of the earth and the descent of man. Those were not the largest, the most interesting, or even the most popular advances of sciences. They were not at all exceptional. No, they were typical scientific ideas; but they were in the one field where every one knew the language. Here therefore the issue between traditional opinion and the new scientific approach could be clearly understood and argued. So today the argument between our accustomed notions of cause and the new concept of chance makes common ground between layman and scientist. And, as in the last century, there are plenty of scientists who hold to the traditional view.

Here more clearly than anywhere, I think, we can see the changing shape of science, and here the layman is most nearly on equal terms with the scientist, because the new ideas are new to both. But to have a clear notion of what is to come in science, and to see what the change means, we must understand how narrowly founded is the accustomed idea of cause and effect. That is why I have spent time on its history. Historically, the turning point was the Scientific Revolution in the seventeenth century. But that revolution went deeper; the concept of causality was only a by-product of it; and though until now it has seemed the logical product, this turns out not to be so. It seemed so because the outstanding success of the Scientific Revolution was to unify in one theory the mechanics of billiard balls and planets. But science is not all astronomy; it is not even all billiard balls, though the nineteenth century was able to build from them a working picture of the behaviour of gases.

More clearly than any one else, it was the French

thinkers of the *Encyclopédie* who drew the conclusion that all scientific prediction is like astronomical prediction. Given the whereabouts and the speeds of all the heavenly bodies at this instant, Newton had said, we can predict their movements from now to eternity. If that is so, said the French mathematician Laplace, then imagine yourself given the whereabouts and the speeds at this instant of every atom in the universe. Given all these, you can forecast the fate of the universe, its molecules and its men, its nebulae and its nations, from now into eternity. And more than this: you can go backward in time as well as forward, and reconstruct the past to eternity. Of course, the hope of actually carrying out such a calculation is rather fanciful. Nevertheless, science to Laplace remained the discovery of causal laws which help us to approach to this hope more and more nearly.

Laplace saw the lavish implications of this view clearly and he stated them boldly. This view has always been faced with some difficulties, particularly in finding a place for human action; and various dialectics and finesses have been invented to avoid them. It has been suggested, for example, that there are moments when the natural laws alter abruptly, and an increase of quantity tips over into a change of quality. But since it is still postulated that these critical steps are fully determined in time and in character by what has gone before, and that the new laws are caused by these changes, there is no real break in causality. There is an abrupt turn, but given all the facts Laplace asked for, even the turn is calculable.

These devices therefore do not deny a belief in complete and universal causality. They make the work of the computer more difficult, forward or backward in time. But they do not change its nature; it remains a purely mathematical task of solving some hypothetical array of equations of motion. Such devices complicate the belief in causality, but they do not change it, and in the last century they could not be allowed to change it.

4

There are several reasons why this belief will no longer do. The reasons are of different weight, and I myself am most impressed by a reason which is not conclusive, but which does shake my own confidence and must I think shake that of others. Here we have been thinking for nearly three hundred years that if there is one causal law which is certain beyond all challenge, it is the law of gravitation. The whole tradition of causality derives from its triumph. Over a hundred years ago, in 1846, when the distant planet Uranus seemed not to be keeping time, we took it for granted that some unseen planet still further away must be disturbing by its it gravitational force. Two men, Adams in England and Leverrier in France, working with no knowledge of one another, and with nothing but pencil, paper, and Newton's laws, calculated where such a planet must be. And when the great telescope at Berlin was turned to the spot, on the day Leverrier's calculations were received, there was Neptune clear to the eye, and spectacular in its vindication of the unalterable laws of gravitation.

And yet, and yet, the laws of gravitation have gone. There is no gravitation; there is no force at all; the whole model was wrong. All that theory was no more than a happy approximation to what really happens. When Newton brought in force as a cause, he was giving to matter the human property of effort, as much as Aristotle once gave it human will. The true causes are now embedded in the nature of space and the way in which matter distorts space; and they have no resemblance to the causes in which we believed for nearly three hundred years. Ironically, Adams and Leverrier merely postponed the catastrophe by sixty years. For one beginning of the crisis in classical physics about 1900 was an oddity like the one which they had set out to explain; only now it was the planet Mercury which was not keeping time – and it was Leverrier himself who discovered this. But search as we might, we could find no new Neptune to blame for the irregularity. It was cleared up only by a radical overhaul of the basic assumptions in Newton's philosophy, particularly in his conception of time.

I have said that this is not a final objection to casual laws. After all, the new theory which Einstein put in place of the old, although as a field theory it is less mechanical than Newton's, is still a causal theory. And Einstein, almost alone among the great physicists of today, continued stoutly to argue on behalf of causality. Yet it does seem to me, for two reasons, that this overthrow of a long accepted cause must deeply shake our confidence. For one thing, the whole conception of causes in science springs historically from the triumph of gravitation. And for another, we see now that it is possible to have every human faith in a causal mechanism, every assurance that this is how nature works, that here is her very action laid bare, and every demonstration that some apparent departure really fits in with that cause – we could have all these, unviolated and gaining in strength for two hundred years. And yet at the end we find that the cause was a fiction. Something else was at work, which has nothing in common with that famous cause. The machine never was a copy of nature. It was only a kind of gigantic orrery or planetarium, which got the heavenly bodies to the right places at the right time, but whose causal mechanism was no more like nature's than Ptolemy's itself.

5

Einstein found the flaw in Newton's theory of gravitation by looking into its very heart. There he found the assumption that time and space are given absolutely, and are alike for all observers. But when he thought through the steps by which different observers can actually compare their time in space, he found them at odds with this assumption. We cannot compare the time in two different places without sending a signal from one to the other, which must itself take time in its passage. As a result, Einstein showed that there is no universal 'now'; there is only 'here and now' for each observer, so that space and time are inextricably woven together, and are aspects of a single reality. Moreover, the structure of space in turn cannot be disentangled from the matter which is embedded in it.

In Einstein's Relativity physics then, time is not a strict sequence of universal before and after. Closely spaced events which appear in one order to one observer may appear in the opposite order to another. Hume and John Stuart Mill had insisted long ago that the essence of cause and effect is their sequence: cause must come before and effect must follow after. Thus Einstein's new conception of time itself adds another difficulty to the definition of causality.

However, this difficulty also can be removed, and is not final. The final difficulty comes from another field which is that of small-scale or quantum physics. Einstein made remarkable advances in this field also; indeed, he was given the Nobel Prize in 1921 for his work not in Relativity but in quantum physics.

The fundamental step which created quantum physics had been taken in 1900 by Max Planck, when he discovered that energy, like matter, is not continuous, but appears always in packets or quanta of definite sizes. From the beginning, the ideas of quantum physics could not be matched with the classical mechanics of particles. Fantastic properties had to be given to an electron whenever it sent out or took up a quantum of energy. The difficulties grew until in the 1920s it began to be seen that we simply cannot make a theory to describe these minute happenings and still hope to keep it rigidly laid out in the classical pattern of causes and effects. There is no way at all of describing the present and the future of these tiny particles and events so that they appear completely determined. This was put into a formal principle in 1927 by the German physicist Heisenberg, and given the sensible name of the principle of uncertainty.

Heisenberg showed that every description of nature contains some essential and irremovable uncertainty. For example, the more accurately we try to measure the position of a fundamental particle, of an electron, say, the less certain will we be of its speed. The more accurately we try to estimate its speed, the more uncertain will we be of its precise position. Therefore we can never predict the future of the particle with complete certainty; because as a matter of fact we cannot be completely certain of its present. If we want to predict its future sensibly, then we must allow it to have some uncertainty: some range of alternatives, some slack – what engineers call some tolerance. We may have what metaphysical prejudices we choose, whether the future really and truly, essentially, is determined by the present. But the physical fact about these small-scale events is beyond dispute. Their future cannot be foretold with complete assurance by any one observing them in the present. And of course, once we have any uncertainty in prediction, in however small and distant a corner of the world, then the future is essentially uncertain – although it may remain overwhelmingly probable.

I have said that this principle of uncertainty refers to very small particles and events. But these small events are not by any means unimportant. They are just the sorts of events which go on in the nerves and the brain and in the giant molecules which determine the qualities we inherit. And sometimes the odd small events add up to a fantastic large one. The tricks which physicists are all eagerly playing just now with liquid helium are of this kind. For example, at temperatures near absolute zero you do not have to syphon liquid helium from one bottle into another. If you hold them lip to lip, the helium will creep up the neck of one bottle and down into the other of itself – and, alas, all over the outside of both.

The principle of uncertainty, which gives us one way of looking at the meaning of these tricks, shook us all a good deal. After all, it said that nature could not be described as a rigid mechanism of causes and effects. And I recall again that all the successes of science, Newton's success and those of the nineteenth century, seemed to have been won hitherto by fitting nature with just this kind of machine. To say suddenly that at bottom these causal chains are not true, that the whole thing cannot be done – that seemed a strange discovery, and a disagreeable one.

It was a discovery, and it has had a profound effect. But it does not seem nearly so strange or unsettling now. On the contrary, to my generation the principle of uncertainty seems the most natural and sensible remark in the world. It does not seem to us to have taken the order out of science. It has taken out the metaphysics and left what had long been forgotten, the scientific purpose.

The purpose of science is to describe the world in an

orderly scheme or language which will help us to look ahead. We want to forecast what we can of the future behaviour of the world; particularly we want to forecast how it would behave under several alternative actions of our own between which we are usually trying to choose. This is a very limited purpose. It has nothing whatever to do with bold generalizations about the universal workings of cause and effect. It has nothing to do with cause and effect at all, or with any other special mechanism. Nothing in this purpose, which is to order the world as an aid to decision and action, implies that the order must be of one kind rather than another. The order is what we find to work, conveniently and instructively. It is not something we stipulate; it is not something we can dogmatize about. It is what we find; it is what we find useful.

Let me give an example. One causal mechanism in the breeding of plants is obviously their sex. No one proved that plants have sex until the eve of the Augustan age, sometime about 1694. But men had been breeding plants for thousands of years before that. Over the larger part of the world, man has actually created his culture by turning a few scraggy grasses into the wheats. His methods were not causal ones; but his work was at least as successful as anything that the rationalists of the Augustan age did.

In order to act, it is not necessary to have a metaphysical belief that the rules by which we are acting are universal and that all other rules are just like them. On the contrary, at bottom all general beliefs of this kind are at odds with the principles of science. Laplace believed that if we knew the present completely, we could completely determine the future. This belief had some political and religious force for Frenchmen of the Revolution. But it has no scientific meaning at all. It does not resemble a scientific statement, or for that matter a literary one, because it is not a statement about reality, either now or in the future. There simply is no sense in asserting what would happen if we knew the present completely. We do not, and plainly we never can.

This is precisely what the principle of uncertainty says to modern physics. It makes no assertions at all about whether we could or could not predict the future of an electron, supposing that we knew this or that about its present. It simply points out that we cannot completely know its present. For instance, we can know either its whereabouts or its speed with high precision; but we cannot know both. And, in consequence, we cannot predict its future.

At bottom then, the principle of uncertainty states in special terms what was always known, which is this. Science is a way of describing reality; it is therefore limited by the limits of observation; and it asserts nothing which is outside observation. Anything else is not science; it is scholastics. The nineteenth century was dominated by Laplace's belief that everything can be described by its causes. But this is no less scholastic than the medieval belief that everything is contained in the First Cause.

6

At this stage those to whom causality is second nature are tempted to open a new line of retreat. Why, they say, should we not go on believing in a strictly determined nature anyway? Why must we say that some future event is not determined, simply because science says that it cannot be predicted? Even suppose, as science now insists, that this is not merely a momentary gap. Even suppose that scientists are right and that they will never discover new laws which will make them able to predict these small events. Granted all this, say the doubters: granted that there are material events which can be shown to be unpredictable by any scientific method at all now or in the future. Is that so profound a discovery? Is it indeed a discovery about anything but science itself? Is it more than a demonstration that the methods of science have shortcomings and are limited in scope? Why must we assume that because science cannot uncover the network of cause and effect in nature, therefore this network is not there? After all, even Laplace never supposed that any human being really could calculate the future conclusively from the present, in practice. He was perfectly aware of the practical limitations to scientific prediction. Why cannot we go on holding his view, then, that the future is determined in theory, whether scientists in practice can predict it or not?

Alas, these winning and ingenuous remarks quite miss the point. Of course Laplace did not believe that the future could be punched out from the present on any calculating machine which men could build in practice. But he believed that in principle it could be done, if not by a human then by a superhuman computer. He believed that the future is fully and finally determined. The future as it were already exists in the mathematics; and the world itself is precisely a machine which calculates it by strict mechanical processes.

This is quite different from our own picture of the relation between present and future. Indeed, we would not be able to begin to set up the present on any universal machine like Laplace's, for two reasons. One is that Relativity has pointed out the difficulties in defining the present instant at two points which are far apart in space. And the other is that the principle of uncertainty has made it clear that even at one point the present cannot be defined with unlimited accuracy.

These difficulties state in technical language the difference between our view and Laplace's, which is clearcut and plain in lay terms. It is this. In Laplace's view, science now or in time would know how to calculate the future exactly. It would not be practicable to do so, because the labour would be too great. But that difficulty is merely one of what is humanly manageable. Just so we might say that in theory the whole of human knowledge could be put into the *Encyclopaedia Britannica*, although in practice the staff needed to write it and the paper to print it would be unmanageable. This is fundamentally different from the reason we have for saying that we cannot predict the future exactly, which is this: that we do not know, even in theory, how to set about it. We do not know any laws for forecasting precisely how the future of a single electron will follow from its present. Indeed, we do not know what either its present or its future is precisely. And we can show that this is an essential limitation; no scientific method can exist either to describe or to predict these with final and unbounded accuracy.

But because we do not know, because science cannot know, does this mean that the future is undetermined? Have we not confessed that all this is merely a limitation in description? And why must this mean that there is not a perfectly good mechanism at work, and that our eyesight and microscopes are merely too misty to see its precise working?

This is an attractive suggestion, but I think rather pathetic; because what it really says is that if the questioner has to choose between science and causality, then he prefers to plump for causality. Since causality is merely one of the tools of science, it seems to me absurd to cling to it as a faith once it turns out that it really is not working any more as a tool. Of course, every one is free to prefer his favourite article of faith to the scientific, that is the empirical method. But do not let us imagine that his faith is then anything except a piece of comfortable and customary superstition. To try to make a nice distinction between what science can predict and what is somehow supernaturally determined is a piece of elegant but really quite shameless self-deception. Science is a practical study of what can be observed, and the prediction from that of what will be observed. To say that causes are somehow getting under this observable world, when anything under it is essentially unobservable, is neither helpful nor meaningful; it is just a piece of faithful comfort. We might as well say that the electrons are really pushed about by blue fairies with red noses who know exactly what they are doing, only it happens that every time we look in their direction these fairies instantly hide. If they are essentially unobservable, beyond all hope of future unravelling, then it simply does not make sense to bring them into any system, logical, metaphysical, or even religious.

These considerations are not wholly abstract. We should remember that they have very practical meanings, and are used every day to forecast, within their own limits, practical results. Take so solemn a matter as a piece of potentially explosive uranium-235. A small piece is overwhelmingly unlikely to go off; a large piece is overwhelmingly likely to go off. What is the critical size which separates the one from the other? This is the kind of question which has been answered with outstanding success by the principle of uncertainty. We have seen the success, and although of course it is no more and no less conclusive than that of Adams and Leverrier in finding Neptune, it does show that all this is not just fancy speculation. Or take another instance from nuclear fission; these instances are ironically apt, because Heisenberg was the only great physicist who remained in Germany to work on the Atomic Energy project there, and the German failure was in large part his failure in directing it. Take as another instance then a good home-made lump of plutonium, taking care to keep it below the critical size. We know that rather more than half of it will have undergone radio-active decay in twenty-five thousand years. But we do not know which half is which; we cannot say of any grain whether it will fall into the decayed or the surviving half. There are no physical laws to tell us – and there cannot be. This is the striking point: that it has been established by Johann von Neumann that no causal theory whatever could make such a forecast without doing violence to some of the known and certain facts.

7

We may seem to be reaching an odd contradiction. Science has come a long way since Hobbes first insisted over three hundred years ago on the great reach of the causal principle, and it has come by using this principle. Now I am saying that the principle is itself mistaken; nature is not strictly a succession of causes and their effects. Then how has science been so successful in picturing the world running on the orbits of causal laws? And if we have no causal laws, are we not delivering the world up to pure lawlessness? Are we not abandoning the idea of any science at all?

These are questions which I shall take up in the next chapter. I shall show there that law and certainty are not the same thing, and that it is possible to set up less familiar but quite rigorous laws of chance. And we shall then see that the causal laws are accumulations of these, and owe their success to the fact that they are admirable approximations of those cases where the laws of chance combine to give overwhelming likelihoods.

But here I want to close with a deeper thought. I have said that the main difficulty today, above all in the physical sciences, has been created by the search for causal laws. But this is not the whole story. We have to remember that no scientific method is truly deductive, taking the physical facts and reasoning from them conclusively to the laws which they follow. At the basis of scientific method lies the kind of imagination which Newton used, who defined a world of particles, postulated laws or axioms which these particles individually follow, and then showed that they combine to make a world much like that we know. Newton had no theories of what these ultimate particles are, and it is we who have tried to identify them first with molecules, then with atoms, then electrons and other minute and indivisible constituents of matter. We have failed. If the world is made of electrons and things like them, then it is certain that they do *not* behave like Newton's particles. They behave sometimes like waves and sometimes like particles; they do not have a precise place and speed at the same instant; and they have other oddities. And when we say for instance that whereabouts and speed cannot be exactly observed at the same time, we mean just this limitation: that we cannot make the hypothesis of individual particles and give them at the same time defined places and speeds in our equations.

These difficulties are not wholly to be traced to the search for cause and effect. Rather they arise because we have believed more deeply that all scientific happenings can be broken into smaller and smaller ultimate pieces, and that these pieces each obey causal laws. We have come to assume that any event which did not seem to flow from its antecedents of itself was sure to do so if we broke it into small enough pieces, either of fact or of matter. This analytic process has really been the basis of our notion of determinism. What we now see is that you cannot have both together. You cannot have a model made of minute particles and events, and have each particle and each event running on strictly causal orbits. Cause and effect are large-scale operations. But the analytic process in the end gives rise to a form of law which is different in type – a law of chance in place of cause.

Since this division became plain in physics, it has oddly and unexpectedly been shown to go deeper, to the fundamentals of logic. This is a side of the problem which is still almost unknown even to scientists, because it comes from the most remote part of mathematics, the study of the logical structure of all mathematical systems. It was shown by Gödel in 1931 that even in a purely abstract system of axioms like Euclid's there arise perfectly reasonable questions which have no answers. That is, even in such a tight, tidy, logical, and as it were entirely arithmetical system, it is possible to formulate theorems which cannot be shown to be either true or false. If we think of such a system as working itself out through time, this is equivalent to asking whether the system might reach certain states in the future. And the answer is that we cannot always know; the problem cannot be solved. There are theorems which may or may not be true; and there are states which might or might not be reached; the mathematics can never decide. And this is in a world without microscopes, matter, and indeterminacy, in a world of pure logic. It is indeed a remarkable landslide, this rift in certainty; and its implications will become clear to experimental scientists only slowly, as they learn that a geological fault has been opened in the strata of logic itself.

In the physical and in the logical worlds, what we have really seen happen is the breakdown of the plain model of a world outside ourselves where we simply look on and observe. It has turned out that you can approximate to physics when you make this separation, but there comes a point when the approximation breaks down. When that point was reached in astonomy, Einstein's laws took the place of Newton's. For Relativity derives essentially from the philosophic analysis which insists that there is not a fact and an observer, but a joining of the two in an observation. This is the fundamental unit of physics: the actual observation. And just this is what the principle of uncertainty showed in atomic physics: that event and observer are not separable. Something very much like this has been happening with less publicity in logic. Indeed, a beginning has now been made by von Neumann in developing a system of mathematics, the Theory of Games, which is based on the essentially undetermined and multivalent attitudes of mind which we all keep in our daily worldly relations. All the currents of science flow together in this: that the analytical and impersonal view of the world is failing. Once it was enough to think that the world keeps still and distant while we painstakingly carve it into sections for microscopic examination. But this is a simplification which has now served its turn. We have reached the stage where the world is integrated within itself, and the gap between the observer and the fact cannot be kept open. The basis of this world is the observation. All the difficulties, whether about the behaviour of Mercury or the failure of causality, derive from the separation between the knower and what is known. Only by joining them do we make knowledge.

These are the new and uncomfortable ideas which have been injected in our lifetime into what had seemed the tidily settled world of physics. In practical results they have been enormously successful – if we ought to call Hiroshima a success. They have worked. In theory we have by no means felt their full force yet. They have been a comfort to many people who have taken them to sustain their belief in Free Will, and they have bewildered as many others, because they outrage their common sense. The world makes sense all right; it makes common sense. It is not a glum conspiracy of nonsense or malevolence out of a novel by Thomas Hardy. The humanist may take courage; the world is full of common sense. But common sense is not what we put into the world. It is what we find there.

CHAPTER 6

The Idea of Chance

I

I HAVE repeatedly spoken of science as a language. This analogy seems to me so easy and helpful that I found it most natural to begin this book by comparing science with the English language. It seems to me natural to think of optics, for example, as a language to describe seeing and being seen. As a language, it is uncommon only in the single-minded pains which it takes to avoid other topics: to get rid of the confusion which might be caused by colour blindness, for instance; and to avoid the more attractive topics of wishing and believing. Optics is the language in which seeing is seeing and nothing else – not even believing.

This analogy would not have occurred at all naturally to scientists in the last century. For a language is no more than a code for describing some chosen features of the world. Of course the purpose of language is to arrange with others how we shall act in the world. But in method it remains a description, which names the facts and mimics their arrangement. The nineteenth century would have thought this too modest a view of science. Its best minds did see science as a guide to action. But they were convinced that it helped them to act usefully because it does not merely describe the world: it explains it. And by an explanation they meant a model which follows nature exactly, link by link, along a chain of causes and effects. An animal is precisely a heat engine, they said; or a gas is a collection of small billiard balls; or the brain is a telegraph office. They believed that in the end there is only one scientific method: to set up a system of causes and effects. If science describes, they held, then it describes the cause by its effects; and if it predicts, it predicts the effect from its causes.

I have said at some length that this belief can no longer be sustained. Very well: we are to give up the universal search for causes. What are we to put in their place? For answer, we must go back to beginnings, and repeat something which cannot be said too often. The aim of science is to describe the world in orderly language, in such a way that we can if possible foresee the results of those alternative courses of action between which we are always choosing. The kind of order which our description has is entirely one of convenience. Our purpose is always to predict. Of course, it is most convenient if we can find an order by cause and effect; it makes our choice simple; but it is not essential.

What we are looking for, in science as much as in the day-to-day of our lives, is a system of prediction: is, as it were, a predictor. The principles which guide us in our predictions are in the end nothing more than steps in the calculation. And life is not an examination; we do not get marks for the steps; what matters is getting the right answer. So it is perfectly possible to base a system of prediction on no principle except trying to get the right answer. This is exactly what all plants and animals do. The bat avoids obstacles by shouting at them that shrill cry just beyond my hearing, and then listens for the echo. Whatever system it has for translating the echo into a prediction it has found by evolution, and evolution has found it by trial and error. The radar set does all this more rationally. Yet the steps in its calculations are no better than the bat's; and they are no worse. For instance, the bat and evolution have long discovered that the best wavelengths for range-finding are the centi-

metre waves which the radar set also uses. A man catching a ball is a predictor, or a child flying a kite, or a cat
at a mouse-hole. They remind us that the business of
prediction, and of science, is to get us to do roughly the
right thing at roughly the right time.

2

There is of course nothing sacred about the causal form
of natural laws. We are accustomed to this form, until it
has become our standard of what every natural law
ought to look like. If you halve the space which a gas
fills, and keep other things constant, then you will double
the pressure, we say. If you do such and such, the result
will be so and so; and it will always be so and so. And we
feel by long habit that it is this 'always' which turns the
prediction into a law. But of course there is no reason
why laws should have this always, all-or-nothing form.
If you self-cross the offspring of a pure white and a pure
pink garden pea, said Mendel, then on an average one
quarter of these grandchildren will be white, and three
quarters will be pink. This is as good a law as any other;
it says what will happen, in good quantitative terms, and
what it says turns out to be true. It is not any less respectable for not making that parade of every-time certainty
which the law of gases makes. And indeed, the gas law
takes its air of finality only from the accumulation of just
such chances as Mendel's law makes explicit.

It is important to seize this point. If I say that after a
fine week it *always* rains on Sunday, then this is recognized and respected as a law. But if I say that after a fine
week it rains on Sunday more often than not, then this
somehow is felt to be an unsatisfactory statement; and
it is taken for granted that I have not really got down to
some underlying law which would chime with our habit

of wanting science to say decisively either 'always' or 'never'. Even if I say that after a fine week it rains on seven Sundays out of ten, you may accept this as a statistic, but it does not satisfy you as a law. Somehow it seems to lack the force of law.

Yet this is a mere prejudice. It is nice to have laws which say: this configuration of facts will always be followed by event A, ten times out of ten. But neither taste nor convenience really makes this a more essential form of law than one which says: This configuration of facts will be followed by event A seven times out of ten, and by event B three times out of ten. In form the first is a causal law and the second a statistical law. But in content and application, there is no reason to prefer one to the other. The laws of science have two functions, to be true and to be helpful; probably each of these functions includes the other. If the statistical law does both, that is all that can be asked of it. We may persuade ourselves that it is intellectually less satisfying than a causal law, and fails somehow to give us the same feeling of understanding the process of nature. But this is an illusion of habit. No law ever gave wider satisfaction than the law of gravitation. Yet we have seen that the explanation it gave of the workings of nature was false, and the understanding we got from it mistaken. What it really did, and did superbly, was to predict the movements of the heavenly bodies to an excellent approximation.

3

There is, however, a limitation within every law which does not contain the word 'always'. Bluntly, when I say that a configuration of facts will be followed sometimes by event A and at other times by B, I cannot be certain whether at the next trial A or B will turn up. I may know that A is to turn up seven times and B three times out of ten; but that brings me no nearer at all to knowing which is to turn up on the one occasion I have my eye on next time. Mendel's law is all very fine when you grow peas by the acre; but it does not tell you, and cannot, whether the single second generation seed in your windowbox will flower white or pink. Mendel himself ran into this trouble when he tested his law, because he had to do his experimental work in a rather small monastery garden.

So far, this is obvious enough. It is obvious that if we did know what is to happen precisely next time, then we would at once have not a statistical law, but a law of certainty into which we could write the word 'always'. But this limitation carries with it a less obvious one. If we are not sure whether A or B will turn up next time, then neither can we be sure which will turn up the time after, or the time after that. We know that A is to turn up seven times and B three; but this can never mean that every set of ten trials will give us exactly seven As and three Bs. In fact, it is not possible to write down an irregular string of As and Bs in such a way that every set of ten successive letters which we pick out from it, beginning where we like, is made up precisely of seven of one and three of the other. And of course it is quite impossible to write them down so that any choice of ten letters picked here and there will contain just seven As.

Then what do I mean by saying that we expect A to turn up seven times to every three times which B turns up? I mean that among all the sets of ten trials which we can choose from an extended series, picking as we like, the greatest number will contain seven As and three Bs. This is the same thing as saying that if we have enough trials, the proportion of As to Bs will tend to the ratio of seven to three. But of course, no run of trials, however extended, is necessarily long enough. In no run of trials can we be sure of reaching precisely the balance of seven to three.

Then how do I know that the law is in fact seven As and three Bs? What do I mean by saying that the ratio tends to this in a long trial, when I never know if the trial is long enough? And more, when I know that at the very moment when we have reached precisely this ratio, the next single trial must upset it – because it must add either a whole A or a whole B, and cannot add seven tenths of one and three tenths of the other. I mean this. After ten trials, we may have eight As and only two Bs; it is not at all improbable. It is not very improbable that we may have nine As, and it is not even excessively improbable that we may have ten. But it is very improbable that, after a hundred trials, we shall have as many as eighty As. It is excessively improbable that after a thousand trials we shall have as many as eight hundred As; indeed it is very improbable that at this stage the proportion of As departs from seven out of ten by as much as five per cent. And if after a hundred thousand trials we should get a proportion which differs from our law by as much as one per cent, then we should have to face the fact that the law itself is almost certainly in error.

Let me quote a practical example. One of the French *encyclopédistes* of the eighteenth century, the great naturalist Buffon, was a man of wide interests. His interest in geology and evolution got him into trouble with the Sorbonne, which made him formally recant his belief that the earth has changed since Genesis. His interest in the laws of chance was less perilous, and it prompted him in 1733 to ask an interesting question. If a needle is thrown at random on a sheet of paper ruled with lines whose distance apart is exactly equal to the length of the needle, how often can it be expected to fall on a line and how often into a blank space? The answer is rather odd: it should fall on a line a little less than two times out of three – precisely, it should fall on a line two times out of π, where π is the familiar ratio of the circumference of a circle to its diameter, which has the value 3.14159265.... How near can we get to this answer in actual trials? This depends of course on the care with which we rule the lines and do the throwing; but, after that, it depends only on our patience. In 1901 a minor Italian mathematician, Mario Lazzerini, having taken due care, demonstrated his patience by making well over 3,000 throws. The value he got for π at one stage was right to the sixth place of decimals, which is an error of only a hundred thousandth part of one per cent.

4

This is the method to which modern science is moving. It uses no principle but that of forecasting with as much assurance as possible, but with no more than is possible. That is, it idealizes the future from the outset, not as completely determined, but as determined within a defined area of uncertainty. Let me illustrate the kind of uncertainty. We know that the children of two blue-eyed parents will certainly have blue eyes; as least, no exception has ever been found. By contrast, we cannot be certain that all the children of two brown-eyed parents will have brown eyes. And we cannot be certain of it even if they have already had ten children with brown eyes. The reason is that we can never discount a run of luck of the kind which Dr Johnson once observed when a friend of his was breeding horses. 'He has had', said Dr Johnson, 'sixteen fillies without one colt, which is an accident beyond all computation of chances.' But what we can do is to compute the *odds* against such a run; this is not as hard as Johnson supposed. And from this we can compute the likelihood that the next child will have brown eyes. That is, we can make a forecast which states our degree of uncertainty in a precise form. Oddly enough, it is just here that Mendel's own account of his work is at fault. He assumed in effect that once a couple has had ten brown-eyed children the chance that they may yet have blue-eyed children is negligible. But it was not.

This area of uncertainty shrinks very quickly in its proportion if we make our forecasts not about one family but about many. I do not know whether this or that couple will have a child next year; I do not even know whether I shall. But it is easy to estimate the number of children who will be born to the whole population, and to give limits of uncertainty to our estimate. The motives which lead to marriage, the trifles which cause a car to crash, the chanciness of today's sunshine or tomorrow's egg, are local, private, and incalculable. Yet, as Kant saw long ago, their totals over the country in a year are remarkably steady; and even their ranges of uncertainty can be predicted.

This is the revolutionary thought in modern science. It replaces the concept of the *inevitable effect* by that of the *probable trend*. Its technique is to separate so far as possible the steady trend from local fluctuations. The less the trend has been overlaid by fluctuations in the past, the greater is the confidence with which we look along the trend into the future. We are not isolating a cause. We are tracing a pattern of nature in its whole setting. We are aware of the uncertainties which that large, flexible setting induces in our pattern. But the world cannot be isolated from itself: the uncertainty *is* the world. The future does not already exist; it can only be predicted. We must be content to map the places into which it may move, and to assign a greater or less likelihood to this or that of its areas of uncertainty.

These are the ideas of chance in science today. They are new ideas: they give chance a kind of order: they re-create it as the life within reality. These ideas have come to science from many sources. Some were invented by Renaissance brokers; some by seventeenth-century gamblers; some by mathematicians who were interested in aiming-errors and in the flow of gases and more recently in radio-activity. The most fruitful have come from biology within little more than the last fifty years. I need not stress again how successful they have been in the last few years, for example in physics: Nagasaki is a monument to that. But we have not yet begun to feel their importance outside science altogether. For example, they make it plain that problems like Free Will or Determinism are simply misunderstandings of history. History is neither determined nor random. At any moment, it moves forward into an area whose general shape is known but whose boundaries are uncertain in a calculable way. A society moves under material pressure like a stream of gas; and on the average, its individuals obey the pressure; but at any instant, any individual may, like an atom of gas, be moving across or against the stream. The will on the one hand and the compulsion on the other exist and play within these boundaries. In these ideas, the concept of chance has lost its old dry pointlessness and has taken on a new depth and power; it has come to life. Some of these ideas have begun to influence the arts: they can be met vaguely in the novels of the young French writers. In time they will liberate our literature from the pessimism which comes from our divided loyalties: our reverence for machines and, at odds with it, our nostalgia for personality. I am young enough to believe that this union, the union as it were of chance with fate, will give us all a new optimism.

5

Let me make this point more explicit. It was assumed in the classical sciences of the last century that such a phenomenon as radio-activity, or the inheritance of a blood group, or loss of nerve, or the rise in prices in a time of scarcity, is each the result of many influences; and that step by step these could be taken apart and the phenomenon traced to all its causes. In each case, what was happening could be treated as a laboratory experiment. It could be isolated from those events in the world which had no bearing on it, and lay as it were beyond the box of the laboratory. And within this box, the causes could be studied one by one, much as we study how the volume of a gas changes when the pressure is varied while we keep the temperature the same, and then when the temperature is varied while we keep the pressure the same.

But this picture of the phenomenon in isolation from the rest of the world and from the observer turns out to be false. There comes a time when it will not do any longer even as an approximation. Then it turns out that time and space, which Newton thought absolute, cannot be given physical meaning without the observer. The laboratory cannot exist in a void, and the experiment cannot be put in a box. And as we refine our measurements, the limitations of the observer look larger and larger. The liquid on whose surface the microscope is trained leaps and shivers under the lens, until we can see the Brownian movement of its molecules. The stately flow of the gas is shot through and through with the random darting of its particles. Enlarge the pointer on the dial a millionfold, and the instrument can no longer be read, because the turbulent movement of its atoms shifts the point from instant to instant. The experimental errors are woven into the very substance of the world.

And while all this was going on in the laboratory, nature and society outside were of course thronged with a million larger examples. Everything in the plant and the living body, in earthquakes and the weather, in animal society and human workshops and the prices on the ticker tape, is beyond the control of the neatly designed experiment. There had been a moment in history, an imaginary moment but no less important for that, when the weights falling from the Leaning Tower had been a key to open the secret of the stars. Ever since, the mute laboratory worker had gone on in the faith that his little box would sort out the sun-spot cycle and the coming of the Black Death and the Wall Street crash. The world is a machine, and he would repeat the triumph of Newton and make a model which would act out its fate minute by minute. Adam Smith and Jeremy Bentham and Mill, Hartley and Mesmer and Freud, Zola and Proust and Theodore Dreiser, each in his own way worked a lifetime in that hope.

But there were also men who were faced with particular problems which they could not wait three centuries to take to pieces. They were not always respectable scientific problems. The gambling friends of Pascal and Euler were impatient men. The insurance brokers in Florence and Amsterdam and London did not care about theory; they wanted empirical results. And then, most interesting, at the end of the last century Francis Galton and later Karl Pearson began to look at human characters: size and weight and configuration and growth. They formed no tidy theories like Lombroso's theory of criminal types. They seemed even to have a harsh suspicion of Mendel's theory of inheritance. Rather they looked back to work like that of Laplace and Gauss, who had first considered what errors must be regarded as unavoidable even in astronomical observation. Thus they came to formulate the notion of the chance distribution of a set of characters in a population. And from their work in turn has developed the whole theory of statistical differences, which I believe to be the basis of science for the future.

Let me quote an example from my own experience. In 1945 I went to Japan, and since I did not speak Japanese there were sent with my party several full-blooded young Japanese who had been brought up in America. It struck me when we set out that they were on the whole smaller men than the white Americans in the party. When we got to Japan, it struck me forcibly that the Japanese we had brought with us were themselves taller on the whole than the native Japanese. Here were two differences provided by nature and by society which could not be treated by laboratory experiment. Nor were they invariable differences. Although on the average the group of white Americans were taller than the group of Japanese Americans, and these in turn taller than the native Japanese, there were men in each group who overlapped into the others. Indeed, the smallest man I set eyes on was a white American, and there was one tall Japanese American. Nevertheless, I was willing to formulate two personal hypotheses: that the Japanese are by heredity smaller than white Americans, and that Japanese brought up in America are taller than home-grown Japanese, presumably because America provides them with different foods or a different environment.

How do we test such hypotheses? The problem is just like those which Pearson tackled, and the method is due to him and to a brewer with a statistical bent who called himself *Student*. We find the average of each of our three types; and at the same time we calculate from the individuals in each group a measure of the variation round its average which this group itself seems to display. Since in the nature of things we observe only a few members in each group, neither our averages nor our measures of variation are free from error. But in each case, the variation allows us to estimate what is the largest error we are likely to make in measuring these averages. That is, we surround each average as we have measured it by an area of uncertainty. If these three areas of uncertainty do not overlap, then we know with some confidence that my hypotheses were justified. But if two of the areas overlap, then we cannot be sure that the difference between the two averages round which they have been drawn is a real one. We have failed to establish a systematic difference between these two groups, because the random fluctuations within each group, as we have observed them on this occasion, are large enough to swamp the possible difference.

6

This is the essential content of the statistical method. It has many applications, and they differ one from another in the detail of application. But the underlying thought is the same. Essentially the thought depends not on unlimited accuracy in measuring a character, but on judging the accuracy by a measure of the inherent variation from individual to individual which we cannot escape. We look for a trend or systematic difference. The line of this trend will itself be blurred by the unsteady hand of chance or random fluctuation. We cannot get rid of this random scrawl. But we can from it determine a measure of random variation, and use that to draw round the trend an area of uncertainty. If the area is small enough by standards which are agreed between us, then the trend is established, and we know the limits within which it is likely to lie. If the area is too large, and the limits too wide, we have not been able to establish a trend. It may

4

exist, but in this set of observations it has been swamped by the random fluctuations.

Let me take another practical instance. We believe that streptomycin is effective in helping to cure tuberculosis. We base this belief on experiment. But in every experiment, patients are themselves in many stages of the disease; they inevitably receive different doses and respond in different degrees; the whole picture is overlaid by unavoidable variation. Can we extract any positive results in so variable a field? Yes, if we choose our statistical technique intelligently. For example, suppose we have measures of the health of each patient from time to time during treatment. Then we can test the hypothesis that on the whole patients get better as treatment goes on. The first step is to find, by taking straightforward averages after each month of treatment, what seems to be the average improvement in each month. This allows us to draw a line of improvement on our graph. The patients are still widely scattered round this line. But we can measure the scatter or random variation round the line of improvement, and we can compare it with the scatter of all results when we neglect the systematic trend or line. And this will be our criterion for judging whether the line of improvement is a real effect or not. We shall see by how much the total scatter is reduced when we compare it with the scatter round our line. If the reduction is substantial by standards on which statisticians are agreed, then we say that we have found a meaningful effect of the treatment; we call it significant. We shall still need further analysis to assure ourselves that what makes the treatment work is the streptomycin. But if the hypothesis that there is a trend with treatment turns out not to reduce the random scatter in the condition of patients, then we have not established an effect at all; the result fails to reach significance.

This approach is very simple in conception. At bottom, it divides the phenomenon which we observe in a hundred instances round us into two parts. I have called the parts systematic and random, or trend and fluctuation, or effect and chance. But under all these names, there runs essentially the same conception: that we can isolate the effect only to a certain accuracy. To determine whether the effect is real, we have therefore to compare its area of uncertainty with the accuracy to which we can isolate it. We have to judge the effect by the fluctuation to which our estimate is liable. If the effect stands out plainly above the fluctuation, then we have a significant result. We have established an effect, and although the unavoidable fluctuation still surrounds it with an area of uncertainty, we can apply our finding with this small margin or tolerance. But if the effect turns out not to be large when compared with the inherent fluctuation, then we have not established its significance. Even if it exists, its area of uncertainty is too large to be useful. Our only hope then is to do more experiments, since each experiment reduces the area of uncertainty.

The idea of chance as I have explained it here is not difficult. But it is new and unfamiliar. We are not used to handling it. So it does not seem to have the incisiveness of the simple laws of cause and effect. We seem to be in a land of sometimes and perhaps, and we had hoped to go on living with always and with certainly. We may see, again and again, that smokers contract cancer of the lung more often than non-smokers; but we go on feeling (as we nervously console ourselves with a cigarette) that the connexion has not been 'proved'.

Yet I believe that the difficulty is only one of habit. We shall become accustomed to the new ideas just as soon as we are willing and as we have to. And we are having to. On all sides science is crowding into fields of knowledge which cannot be isolated in the laboratory, and asking us to come to conclusions in matters where we cannot hope to trace a causal mechanism. It may seem to be overtaxing our notion of science to hope that we shall find some common method of tackling the problems of physics and economics, of evolution and soil chemistry, of medicine and meteorology, of psychology and aerial bombardment. We have grown accustomed to thinking of science itself as divided into smaller and smaller pieces of specialization, an atomic universe of knowledge of its own, which no one and nothing can again hope to master. But this may well be an illusion. The different branches of science may seem so far apart only because we lack the common method on which they grow and which holds them together organically. Look back to the state of knowledge in the year 1600: the branches of science and of speculation seemed as diverse and as specialized, and no one could have foreseen that they would all fall into place as soon as Descartes and Hobbes introduced the unifying concept of cause and effect. The statistical concept of chance may come as dramatically to unify the scattered pieces of science in the future. What Hobbes and Newton did was to change the whole concept of natural law: instead of basing it on the analogy of the human will, they built it on cause and on force. But this analogy with human effort is now breaking down. We are on the threshold of another scientific revolution. The concept of natural law is changing. The laws of chance seem at first glance to be lawless. But I have shown in this chapter that they can be formulated with as much rigour as the laws of cause. Certainly they can be seen already to cover an infinitely wider field of human experience in nature and in society. And it may be that they will give to that field the unity which the last fifty years have lacked. If they do, they will give us all also a new confidence. We have been swept by a great wave of pessimism, which rises from our own feeling of helplessness in the recognition that none of us understands the great workings of the world. As science and knowledge have been broken into pieces, there has come upon us all a loss of nerve. That happened to the old classical culture of the Mediterranean in the seventeenth century. The future lay with the driving and purposeful optimists of the north, who seized the notion of cause and purpose, and with it conquered nature and the world together. We are looking for another such universal concept to unify and to enlighten our world. Chance has a helpless ring in our ears. But the laws of chance are lively, vigorous, and human; and they may give us again that forward look which in the last half century has so tragically lowered its eyes.

CHAPTER 7

The Common Sense of Science

I

WE have now crossed the tangled uneven fields of science
at several places. More than this, we have at critical
points mined below the surface for the solid strata on
which that rests. I am using the images of exploration
and of search, and they are just, because this halting
step-by-step into the sense of science is a voyage of discovery. And the dimension for this voyage is time. Like
the voyages of the Spaniards into the fabulous West
science even at its boldest does the will of history, and in
turn helps to determine its movement. Like civilization
and like our societies, it exists in the larger setting of
history: it does not exist, it grows. Civilization is less
than ten thousand years old: in this moment of time
man has created the world we know, from Ur to Radio
City, and from Confucius and Pythagoras to Rabelais
and Einstein. And in that short and spirited adventure
science fills a still smaller moment.

Science as we know it indeed is a creation of the last
three hundred years. It has been made in and by the
world that took its settled shape about 1660, when
Europe at last shook off the long nightmare of religious
wars and settled into a life of inquisitive trade and industry. Science is embodied in those new societies; it has
been made by them and has helped to make them. The
medieval world was passive and symbolic; it saw in the
forms of nature the signatures of the Creator. From the
first stirrings of science among the Italian merchant adventurers of the Renaissance, the modern world has

been an active machine. That world became the everyday world of trade in the seventeenth century, and the interests of science were appropriately astronomy and the instruments of voyage, among them the magnet. A hundred years later, at the Industrial Revolution, the interest shifted to the creation and use of power. This drive to extend the strength of man and what he can do in a day's work has remained our interest since. In the last century it moved from steam to electricity. Then in 1905, in that wonderful year when at the age of twenty-six he published papers which made outstanding advances in three different branches of physics, Einstein first wrote down the equations which suggested that matter and energy are interchangeable states. Fifty years later, we command a reservoir of power in matter almost as large as the sun, which we now realize manufactures its heat for us in just this way, by the annihilation of its matter.

These great historical movements must underlie everything that can be said about science. We should be proud of their share in science, and of the share which science has had in them. And in them the actual influence, the interpenetration of all our actions, goes deeper than the mere surface of society, the radar screen, the indirect heating, and the vitamin pill of our century, or the white bread, the leather shoes, the cotton dress, and the iron bedstead of the Industrial Revolution. Science has entered into the life and structure of society, so that the man who makes a living in a kitchen garden in Kent and the man who draws strips about blonde heroines in space-ships can be seen equally to owe their market to our technical society. And if the one is not allowed to employ boys of ten, and the other must spice his cartoons with glib and sexy tortures, that sensibility, good and bad, is largely the creation of science. Human life is social life, and there is no science which is not in some part a social science.

For this reason, I have looked at the ideas of science always in the setting of their times. From year to year they grow larger until at last the outline is quite changed. And the growth does not go on in empty space, it does not even go on in an abstract space where there is nothing but ideas. It goes on in the world, the rational and empirical world. The mastery and the greatness of science rest in the end on this, that here the rational and the empirical are knotted together. Science is fact and thought giving strength to one another.

2

But we ought at last to make a map of the land we have explored; and here it is time to put aside history and the other aids to navigation. Even in following the stages by which science has grown, we have come in the last chapters more and more to ask, What is the basis of scientific method today? And it is now time to sum up what we have found when our journey has brought us to the present.

The map we are making is as it were a geological map; it plots the strata on which our technical skill rests. For the skill of head and hand go together. As the instrument makers and engine builders of the eighteenth century showed, our understanding of nature can only be as accurate as the machine parts with which we explore and control her. And equally, as the whole progress of quantum physics has shown from the first equations of Max Planck in 1900 to the atomic piles of today, our technical success rests on skill and boldness of mind in thinking through the implications of experiment with no regard to our habits of philosophy – whether these habits are sceptical or materialist.

Whether they are sceptical or materialist, these habits are founded deeply in the way we have long come to think that science must conceive the real world. We are all aware, although we rarely think about it, that all human forethought depends on our recognizing or putting some kind of order into the world. As much as book-keeping, government, and doing the week-end shopping, science is an activity of putting order into our experience. So much was true even of the science of Aquinas. To this was added in the sixteenth and seventeenth centuries a new assumption about the kind of order which science sets out to find or make. Roughly, the assumption amounts to this: that science is to get rid of angels, blue fairies with red noses, and other agents whose intervention would reduce the explanation of physical events to other than physical terms. The world is regular in itself; the world is a machine.

In order to simulate the workings of this machine, we usually describe a model made of simple units and obeying simple laws whose motions are then shown to take it to just those points in time and space where experiment can check it against the physical world. It does not matter whether this model is made with pulleys and springs and cathode tubes whose behaviour has become familiar to us, or whether it is simply an array of equations to be solved. Either is a model. The true essence of the model is that it is an axiomatic construction like that of Euclid. It postulates that the world is built out of repeated units, atoms or cells or reflexes, which obey defined laws and whose behaviour is then simply the action of these laws through time.

Finally we have come to take it for granted that these laws must have very much the shape of Euclid's axioms. Euclid's axioms determine what happens when you draw a given configuration of lines, and they determine it precisely and once for all. If three lines are drawn which meet by pairs in three different places, then they enclose a triangle and its angles add up to one hundred and eighty degrees. They do not enclose a triangle half the time, and something else the other half. The angle is not one hundred and eighty degrees seven times out of ten, and something else three times. And the angle is not nearly a hundred and eighty degrees, within some area of uncertainty. In Euclid's world, everything happens as has been foretold. Or so mathematicians thought, until the recent flutter caused by the existence of theorems which cannot be proved to be either true or false. Of course, Euclid's world happens to contain no time; and this is a difference of far-reaching meaning. Nevertheless, we have grown accustomed for three hundred years to think all laws like his: precise, determinate, and invariable. In a world with time in it, they are causal laws. And these are the laws which we have thought to be of the essence of science.

That background I have marked in detail in this book. And I have added to it in detail again another kind of law which can be put into a working world. This world will still be orderly, a machine, and it can have a model, although it need not. It differs essentially in being moved by laws which have a different form: the form of chance in place of cause and effect. But in the map which we are now making, we should look deeper than this. We should look below the differences in method, to their origin in the nature of science as we now see it. What is the nature of science? That is our question in this chapter. From its answer the new methods of science must be seen to grow directly. And here our speculation must be most searching and original.

3

If we are to begin at the beginning, we must grasp that we are all part of the world we observe. We cannot divide the world into ourselves on one side of the screen as spectators, and everything else as a spectacle on the other side, which we remotely observe. This may seem merely a philosophical point. And it is of course possible to put together a good approximate working science on a false philosophy: to make steam engines and to fix the nitrogen in the air and solve several differential equations. But there comes a point of fineness when these rough and ready habits fail; and then it is not possible to get the right answers until we have the right notion of what it is that we are doing. At this point our philosophy must be right, if philosophy is the word for this critical attitude to our own habits of thought. We must look not at some abstract view of science, but at the actual processes which we carry through when we practise science.

I have already recalled the most remarkable practical example of this. Physicists since Newton have been describing the world as a network of events. But physics does not consist of events; it consists of observations, and between the event and us who observe it there must pass a signal – a ray of light perhaps, a wave, or an impulse – which simply cannot be taken out of the observation. This is the insight which Einstein showed in 1905. It came to him when, looking at the discrepancies within physics then, he asked himself how in fact one would set about doing what Newton took for granted, namely comparing the time in two places far apart. Once the question is put, every one can answer it: you cannot make any comparison at two different places without sending a signal and observing its arrival. The insight is not in answering the question; it was in asking it. Event, signal, and observer: that is the relationship which Einstein saw as the fundamental unit in physics. Relativity is the understanding of the world not as events but as relations.

Something like this had been said by philosophers for some time: that science must get rid of abstractions, and make its system only out of what is in fact observed. But Einstein was the first to take the philosophy seriously. He put it into equations; and within a few years, physicists were astonished to find that it explained the erratic behaviour of Mercury, and predicted the bending of light near the sun.

I stress this example from large-scale physics for this reason. Examples are often quoted from quantum physics to show that our very act of observing them affects the particles we are looking at, much as a rabbit scurries away from our headlights at night. In the same way, it is hard in the social sciences to take a poll of opinion and frame the question so that it does not bias the replies. And in psychology the method of asking oneself questions has now been shown to be most fallible: you cannot watch your own mind and pretend to yourself that you are not looking. Yet none of these difficulties is as fundamental as that which Einstein revealed. In these examples, observation merely intrudes into the experiment. But Relativity went deeper and showed that the observations are the bricks and stuff of science.

By habit, this is not an easy point to grasp. We accept it during the experiment, and when that is over we slip back into making some model whose pieces are not observations but idealized things. Why not? we ask, It is only a model. And indeed, it will work well enough as an approximate model of large events, such as eclipses and hydro-electric dams and the action of penicillin in arresting the multiplication of bacteria. But when we come to finer effects we must be more modest and more realistic.

For then we must use science as it is, and that is an assembly of observations so ordered that they tell us what we may expect to observe in the future.

4

In using the word observation, I am conscious still of having drawn too passive a picture of the process of science. We may be tempted still to think of the world as going its mighty way and merely impressing on the scientist in passing a glimpse from time to time of its imperturbable motion. This would be a grave misunderstanding. Indeed it would perpetuate the breach between the world and the experimenter which I have been trying to close. Science is not only rational; it is also empirical. Science is experiment, that is orderly and reasoned activity. The essence of experiment and of all science is that it is active. It does not watch the world, it tackles it.

This of course is not peculiar to science. All living is action, and human living is thoughtful action. If this is plain enough as a statement about living, it still needs to be underlined about science: that science is a characteristic activity of human life. The characteristic of human action is that it is a choice at each step between what are conceived to be several alternative courses open to us. Men can visualize these alternatives and animals probably cannot; but in both, action means choice – and this, whether we suppose the choice to be free or circumscribed. In both, action is directed towards the future. Men are conscious of this direction, and choose one action rather than another in the conscious hope that it will lead to one rather than another kind of future. I add that this statement describes what they do correctly, whether we think that their choice is free or determined.

This seems to me the most important point which I can make; and oddly enough, it has had least attention in the past. The characteristic of living things is that their actions are directed towards the future. We could put this more bluntly, and say that it is simply the characteristic of action; but this seems to me a needless abstraction, since action and living are in effect interchangeable notions. Living things change; they are different tomorrow from what they were today; and their actions today are directed towards tomorrow. The enzymes in the cell are unaware that what they do will make the cell divide in twenty minutes from now; but if they fail to do it, neither they nor the cell has a future; both die. We do not know what sets in motion the life cycle of the thread worm or the liver-fluke or the oak; but we know that each stage of that cycle is a getting ready for the next; and if the organism misses one cue, it dies. The mechanism of getting ready is odd and elaborate: we see the shadow and close our eyes, we hear a noise and our glands squirt adrenalin into our blood, so that the pulses quicken, the muscles tense, and the nerves are alert. But in every case our actions are directed towards some obscurely foreseen future. And this is true of the most primitive cell, and of Gibbon mining mountains of scholarship for the pleasure at last of minting one ringing footnote.

All this is hidden in the process of life; but it becomes plain and explicit when we look for scientific laws. For of course a scientific law is a rule by which we guide our conduct and try to ensure that it shall lead to a known future. The law formulates our anticipation of the future in a systematic way, as a kind of shorthand. And the wider the conditions in which the law applies, and the more compact as it were its shorthand, the more powerful and remarkable we think the law. But a scientific law differs from our own habitual way of pointing our actions towards the future only in being more systematic and explicit. We are all forward-looking creatures. Life is a process of looking forward. It turns towards the future as mites shift towards the light. Indeed, living things alone go through processes, such as age and decay, by which the future can plainly be told from the past. They make time visible; whereas there is nothing in the dead world at all easily accessible to tell the past from the future. In classical mechanics time has no recognizable direction, and the universe would work just as well if every atom in it were rolling backwards.

5

The key to the action of living things then is this, that it is directed towards the future. They have a way of knowing what is going to happen next, or more precisely, how to act in anticipation of what is going to happen next. Most of this knowledge is unconscious. We need not be astonished about this foresight, or at any rate we need not find it more astonishing than we find the rest of the world. For plainly it has always been the condition for the survival of living things, individually and in species. Unless they could adapt themselves to the future, and interpret its signals in advance, they were bound to perish. Whatever the rhythm and the uniformities of nature, what has survived of life has necessarily had to be in tune throughout; this chiming has been the condition for survival. Galileo is said to have discovered that a pendulum keeps nearly steady time by timing a swinging lamp, in 1583 in the cathedral of Pisa, by his pulse. The story makes my point in a neat symbolic manner; for of course all that Galileo or my doctor or any one else has discovered is, not that either the pendulum or the pulse keeps steady time, but that they both keep the same time. Whatever their rhythm, they keep the same rhythm. We find the world regular as we find it beautiful, because we are in step with it.

I have said that in using foresight, whether unconsciously in instinct and habit or consciously in inference, living things have had to adapt themselves or die out. And we could put this more trenchantly: the act of foresight is itself the adaptation to the future. By this act individuals adapt themselves, and so do societies and all living assemblies. So the adaptation of a species is a slow action directed towards the future, in which the whole society interprets the signals, whether of the coming ice-age or of the erosion of a continent, and unconsciously changes its structure to meet the change.

I repeat the word 'unconsciously' because of course there is nothing in this which need be rationally understood or consciously willed. For the species as a whole, the mechanism of adaptation may be quite impersonal, and may even be at odds with the survival of the individual, as is the bee's dying sting. Selection inevitably acts now, and yet the species inevitably is adapting itself to the future: the generations prepare, each for the next. We need see no master mind behind this and no driving purpose. It is I repeat the condition of life for the individual and the species. The present is not like the future, but it is not unlike it either; it is a signal of the future; and living things, singly or in species, are predictors which interpret the signal so that they make ready for the future.

The idea of a machine which is a predictor is altogether new. But it is of outstanding importance, and we must become used to it. It covers all the basic actions of living things, from the search for food in the lowest cell to the boldest creations of the human imagination. To my mind, it gives us an insight into the function and processes of the human mind which has been missed by older philosophies. And this is not to be wondered at, because it is hard to grasp the full scope of a predictor until you have tried to build one.

A predictor is a machine which uses information about the past and the present in order to make ready for the future. In the nature of things, neither its information nor its forecasts can be complete. But they do not seek to be: the predictor is not trying to be a pocket version of the hypothetical angel of Laplace, a sort of scientific Tiresias who knows everything and has foreseen everything. A predictor takes its information in the form of signals, and its mechanism interprets these signals so that it acts in anticipation of the future. This action is a continuous process. The predictor goes on accepting signals even while it is adjusting itself towards the future, and it feeds these back into the mechanism so that, as it were, it keeps on tracking the future from moment to moment. This picture will do equally well for a predictor which is in fact tracking an aircraft so that the guns may fire on it at the right instant, or for the bat sending out its short-wave note to detect obstacles, or for the mechanisms which keep our body temperature constant or send blood to the brain when we are thinking. What I have called the interpretation of these signals is itself a fascinating business, because in every mechanical system, living or constructed, it implies a sorting out of the meaning of the message from the meaningless oscillations which are carried with it. But I want rather to single out the essential relation: that the present provides a set of signals, which are made continuously to yield a meaning from which the future is anticipated. At each moment the machine must integrate its signals as a whole; the function of the process is a synthesis, not an analysis.

6

We are interested in science, where the process of prediction is conscious and rational. Even in human beings this is not the only kind of prediction. Men have sound intuitions which have certainly not been analysed into rational steps, and some of which may never be. It may be for example, as is sometimes claimed, that most people are a little better at guessing an unseen card, and some people much better, than would be a machine which merely picks its answers by chance. This would not be altogether surprising, for, whatever the human mind is, it is certainly not a machine making only chance guesses, like a table of random numbers. Certainly evolution has selected us rapidly because we do possess gifts of foresight much above those of other animals. The rational intelligence is one such gift, and is at bottom as remarkable and as unexplained. And where the rational intelligence turns to the future, and makes inferences from past experiences to an unknown tomorrow, its success is quite as great a mystery as the very modest successes of even the most gifted guessers – off the music hall stage – who have yet been found.

There are two points here which we need to see very clearly. The first is an old confusion. For two hundred years now, philosophers have distinguished between reasoning by pure deductive processes, such as is found in Euclid, and inductive reasoning which extends the experience of the past into the future. But this distinction is much overrated. All that can be said about deduction is that we can state its processes, and give rules for deciding what is acceptable, in a precise form. But the sanctions for believing that its conclusions will be true tomorrow because they were true yesterday are no different from those which apply to any other theory which claims to reach into the future. If a triangle has three equal sides, then its three angles will be equal, we say. But what we mean is still that the three angles *are* equal; we have deduced that they are so by steps of logic which have always yielded sound results. If we say that the three angles will be equal, then we claim that these steps will continue to be allowable and will yield true results in the future. And this claim is typically an induction from the past to the future.

The second point goes even deeper. There is an unspoken assumption in all our speculations that the ideal of science is to make predictions which shall always be fulfilled. We are hankering after the Laplace predictor, which shall be a perfect machine to get all the answers right. This is equivalent to saying that we want a model which shall be indistinguishable from the real world at every observation. This is not the aim of any predictor. Here bluntly we have the difference between the model and the predictor; and this is why I brought in the word 'predictor': because it is not a machine which claims to act out the future in advance. It tries to forecast it, by its own process. And its forecasts are not always right. It does not assume the future already to exist, to be dredged or conjured up in advance at our bidding. It makes no larger claim than that the future can in general be predicted, within defined limits of uncertainty. And since there are uncertainties, the predictor will sometimes be wrong.

We must face this fact, that in the nature of things predictions sometimes turn out wrong. Naturally, our aim is to have them right as often as possible and at least more often than not. But forecasts can be useful even if they are quite often wrong. We joke about the weather forecasts, but it was necessary to keep them secret during the war. And in major biological processes like evolution, the mistaken prediction has an important function.

Genetic factors which remain in a species even though
their effect is to make it less well fitted to its environment
are a kind of mistake in prediction, and as it were a
residual error. Yet without them, the species cannot
adapt itself to new changes. Some heavily armoured
monsters have probably died out for lack of these means
of future adaptation, just as the pure strains of white
mice would die outside the laboratory for which they
have been bred to excessive perfection. Fitness for use
must retain an element of unfitness and elasticity in
order that it may also be fitness for change. When
Bolingbroke and Paley argued that man is designed like a
watch, which fits its use perfectly, they had no thought of
further evolution. Characteristically, the eighteenth century was for them the peak and the point of rest of
nature's history.

By contrast, we have learned to see the world in motion
and in change. We are clearer about our own shortcomings, but we have also learned not to stop at them
smugly. For what is true of the species when it faces the
future is true of the individual. Both adapt themselves to
the future by continued correction, as a predictor does.
The process is one of trial and error. This is the process
we call learning, and the errors are as essentially part of
it as the successes. If you put a mouse into a maze and
it gets it right first time, it has not learned to run the maze.
It does not learn until it makes some mistakes and learns
to avoid them. One mouse may learn from its mistakes
more quickly than another, but not even the ideal mouse
of the psychology laboratory can learn otherwise than by
making some mistakes.

The process of learning is essential to our lives. All
higher animals seek it deliberately. They are inquisitive
and they experiment. An experiment is a sort of harmless
trial run of some action which we shall have to make in

the real world; and this, whether it is made in the laboratory by scientists or by fox-cubs outside their earth. The scientist experiments and the cub plays; both are learning to correct their errors of judgement in a setting in which errors are not fatal. Perhaps this is what gives them both their air of happiness and freedom in these activities.

We must therefore understand that it is the nature of predictions to be sometimes mistaken. It is only so that we learn as individuals and as species. And science learns in the same way. This is precisely the step which Galileo and Francis Bacon took more than three hundred years ago, which was the beginning of our science. For until they set the Scientific Revolution going, men held to the medieval belief that the workings of nature could be understood by intellectual insight alone. Galileo and Bacon coupled with this appeal to reason a new appeal to fact. Since then, the test of scientific explanation has in the last place always been empirical: does it match the facts? Science itself has therefore been conceived, though unconsciously, as a process of learning; for to appeal to fact in speculation is to grant the possibility of error. Science is a predictor mechanism in process of continual self-correction. The steps from Ptolemy's astronomy to Newton's and thence to Relativity are precisely stages of learning; each step corrects the small but demonstrable error which has opened between prediction and fact. Let us not be contemptuous of mistakes; they are the fulcrum on which the process of life moves. At the very time that Paley was tracing God's design in the watch-like perfection of man, William Blake said more modestly, but with deeper insight, 'To be an Error & to be Cast out is a part of God's design.'

7

The fundamental ideas which I have been putting forward are these. Every living action is an act of choice. It is directed towards the future. The machine which we conceive within it is a predictor, which interprets past and present information as signals to accommodate itself to an expected future. And interpretation and accommodation cannot be made altogether free from error, for error is essential to the process of learning which directs them.

There is in all this a bold analogy between the way in which individuals learn, the way in which species adapt themselves, and the way in which science works. But, of course, it is my point that this is not merely an analogy: it is a true and close relation. For science is not a special activity. It is a type of all human activity. An Italian who goes to New York soon learns to adapt his habits to eating a factory-made cereal for breakfast. There is some evidence that the cereal eaters, as a group, are adapting their jaws to their diet by the slow workings of natural selection. But between these extremes there lies the equally human activity of scientific development. The invention and popularization of the breakfast cereal is itself a scientific solution to a complex of problems, which range all the way from cutting down the time between getting out of bed and catching the train, to the full use of the most readily won foods of North America.

What marks out science as a system of prediction and adaptation from those of the individual and of the species is at bottom this, that it is a method which is shared by the whole society consciously and at one time. This at once implies that science must be communicable and systematic. Both the signals and the predictions must be of a kind which every one can have in common. To my mind, philosophers put the cart before the horse when they say that science constructs a world by sorting out what the experiences of different people have in common. On the contrary, the practice of science supposes the existence of a real and a common world, and assumes that its impact on each individual who is part of it is modified by him in a way which constitutes his personal experience. We do not construct the world from our experiences; we are aware of the world in our experiences. Science is a language for talking not about experience but about the world.

But what is most striking about the predictions of science is that they are not an assembly of piecemeal guesses. Science is a way of ordering events: its search is for laws on which to base the single predictions. This is the stroke which rounds our picture: that science is systematic in method because it seeks a system of prediction. The aim of science is to order the particular example by articulating it on a skeleton of general law.

Once again, what I have said about science is not peculiar to it. All human conduct is shaped by what the individuals believe to be general laws. The human predictor interprets the signal by an act of recognition which puts it into some general category. We then assume that the future will have some general likeness with futures we have met before which followed this kind of signal, and this is the kind of future we prepare for. We recognize a pair of dumb-bells and brace ourselves to lift them; when they turn out to be made of cardboard, the shock is unpleasant because unexpected. What is odd about the generalizations of science is not even that they are far wider, and cover a range of facts beyond the habits of any one individual. This is a real difference, but it is not the essential difference. The essential difference is that the generalizations of science are explicit. And this derives at once from the fact that science is communicated. The individual need never make a list of his habits, that is his generalizations, because he does not need to pass them on to any one else. He will form habits of anticipating the future from present signals even if he never expects to meet another person. Robinson Crusoe did so; and Defoe shows striking psychological insight when he describes the disorder into which Crusoe was thrown when he saw the footprint, not because Crusoe feared the presence of other people, but because their presence had ceased to be part of his conceptual world. Although we cannot be sure, it is likely that some animals lack any form of communication; yet it is certain that they still form habits.

It is the explicit character of its laws which makes science a different activity; and this character derives from communication. Science is the activity of learning by a whole society, even though that society may so divide its labour that it passes the responsibility for this activity to a few men. And the laws of science are those principles of prediction and adaptation to the future which apply to the whole society, and can be learned by all its members in explicit form. This need to meet two requirements at once, universal usefulness and explicit statement, is precisely what makes a world pictured by science seem strange to our personal experience. As persons we will not find ourselves analysing the world into cells and co-enzymes and mesons and genes and curved space, because that is not an individual's analysis of his own experience. And precisely the individual's analysis of his own experience is the subject of discourse in Berkeley and Hume and McTaggart and Moore, whose philosophies all start from a point inside the head of one person. It is not to be wondered at that science and philosophy have more and more been losing touch when they have been talking about such different things. The nucleus and energy and the central nervous system are entities which are reached as we seek for the common world under the random fluctuations of individual experience. And the odd properties which they have are part of the price we pay for making them explicit. The world impinges on our experience in ways which we can recognize implicitly for ourselves as design, meaning, and cause and effect, and these will do admirably as approximations to the experience of all of us. But when we try to refine this language to describe in detail the real world which underlies our experiences, we meet the difficulties of all language. No explicit statement, no communicable language can formulate generalizations which are more precise than the common agreements between those who use them. So we cannot make scientific laws which have a greater finality than the measurements and rules which we can share. Our laws of prediction are limited by our human and necessary errors. There is nothing pathetic about this; it is no more tragic a shortcoming than others which make us men and not something else, than hunger or ambition. These are the nature and the driving forces of human societies; and I have shown that error in the laws of science also partakes of both.

8

The basis of the map which I have drawn in this chapter has been the relation between present and future. It is as if the future were our North and Pole-star: this gives their direction and their structure to the act and the thought, in life and in science. I am therefore not much troubled by the difficulties which philosophers have in trying to rationalize the process of intellectual inference or induction. Philosophers have wanted to give to induction about the future the same status that deduction holds in a timeless science like geometry. And I have already remarked that, as soon as deduction is used in a science which takes account of the passing of time, it has no higher status than has induction.

More generally the philosopher and the man in the street begin their speculations by thinking about the past and the present, as a solid basis of knowledge. For two reasons, this is not useful. First, it is only the past and the present of our own experience which are known. The real world which we share with others is just as mysterious in the past and the present as in the future. And second, it is a mistake to suppose that the basic process in thought is looking back at what is known; and that looking forward to the future is to be justified from this. This is a reversal of the process of life. Anticipating the future is the fundamental activity; babies do it before they are born. Analysing the past and the present is a subsidiary process, whose purpose is still that we shall learn to recognize and interpret signals for the future. It is absurd to ask why the future should turn out to chime with our knowledge of the past. This puts the question upside down, and makes nonsense of it. What we have learned from the past is knowledge only because the future proves it to be true.

The only question which can sensibly be asked about the method of induction into the future is this. What are our grounds for preferring one prediction to another? Why do we choose this rather than that course of action, in circumstances where the future which we foresee remains uncertain whichever we follow? It is not enough to answer that one prediction has a smaller calculated area of uncertainty than the other; for like every scientific law, this calculation already assumes a preference, if not between these forecasts then between more fundamental ones. And it certainly will not do to say that one prediction has proved to be right more often than the other; because the next event is not the same as the last, and there is in fact no way of comparing events as such. No, our preference is not between forecasts but between *ways* of forecasting. We are not preferring one prediction, but one scientific law to another. And laws of course, unlike events, can be weighed by past evidence – although we ought to beware of the word 'past': what we really mean is by *other* occasions on which we predicted the future on the basis of these laws.

One of the difficulties which have troubled philosophers and men in the street on all such issues, is that they have had so static a picture of the future. They have thought of the future as like the past or present, simply a moment along an endless red carpet of time, unrolling before us and rolling up behind. The future is just like the present, they have said; it just happens to be at another time. This error derives from Newton's picture of time, which had no direction at all, and might as well have run backwards. But since the end of the last century, there has been known one physical property which gives a direction to time. It is this. If you look at a stream of gas which has come out of a nozzle, you can tell which part of the gas is further from the nozzle, that is which has come out earlier, without seeing the nozzle. The part which flowed out earlier is by now more disorderly, and its molecules are drifting about more at random. They have lost the direction imposed by the flow through the nozzle. So the passage of time in the universe at large is marked by an increasing state of physical disorder or randomness. It is remarkable that this is itself a chance effect, yet only this gives time (and with it cause and effect) its direction.

The essential point is that this distinguishes the future

from the past: it is the one general law about the future to which we are all attuned. We do not know how we sense this; but we certainly do. Indeed, the essential property of life is that it is opposed to this current: life imposes greater order from moment to moment, while the physical universe is drifting into greater disorder. Even the guessing of an unseen card is not beyond the boundaries of the intelligible, once we understand that the future has distinctive properties which make it recognizably different from the present. Recognizably different, in the statistical sense: for the future differs from the present by being statistically more random. The guess would be inexplicable only if it were always right.

CHAPTER 8

Truth and Value

I

PEOPLE who are troubled in mind by the changes which
they see science working in their world usually single out
the technical changes: the aeroplane, the bomb, the
habit of reading newspapers, the shift from homely com-
forts and home music to television. But under these
changes there runs in us all a deeper division between
the social habits of our schooldays and new habits of
thought. We are troubled by a two-sidedness in our own
behaviour, where one side is what we have long been
taught to value, and the other is worldly success. We are
faced every day with actions of which our own code of
conduct makes us ashamed, but which we find compel-
ling if we are to battle with the hard facts of society.

We do not consciously blame science for this rift until
it throws out some unavoidable challenge, such as in our
time has been set by the atomic bomb. But that sharp
issue is merely a symbol. Beyond all our actions stands
the larger shadow: how are we to choose between what
we have been taught to think right and something else
which manifestly succeeds? And this empirical test of
success grows more pressing as we grow used to it in
science. The empirical habit never lets the traditional
beliefs alone for long, even within science. And it has
been busy now for quite six hundred years in changing
the accepted codes of good and right conduct.

For of course, these codes have not remained fixed
since the days of William of Ockham. The ideals of what
is good have suffered slow but remarkable changes, even

in the same Church. It is plain enough that the ideals of
the Renaissance are not the same as those of the Fathers,
and more recently, that the Protestant virtues differ from
the Catholic, which have themselves changed. The medieval doctrine of the just price had been deeply made
over before a Pope could write *Rerum Novarum* in 1891.
And we see what has become of the Christian virtues in
the Methodism of the early nineteenth century: how
the stress has shifted from charity and loving kindness,
quite unconsciously, to the socially powerful virtues of
thrift, sobriety, frugality, and independence. So we are
in a state of change today not because we have let go of
some ancient absolute of perfection, but because like
every age our age is trying to re-discover its own
conscience.

Nor is science the only ferment at work. I have said
again and again in this book that science is a part, a
characteristic part, of human activity at large. I have
been at pains in the last chapter to show scientific method as the method of all human inquiry, which differs
at last only in this, that it is explicit and systematic. This
is very striking when we come to problems of right judgement and good conduct. There never has been a great
book or a powerful work of art which has not been
thought immoral by those with an older tradition. Jews
still think the New Testament immoral, and Christians
the Koran. Savonarola thought Florentine art licentious,
and when George Eliot wrote about him in the last century, she thought him licentious and her critics thought
her so. Sidney's *Apologie for Poetrie* is a school book now,
and so is Shelley's *Defence of Poetry*. Yet Sidney was de-
fending all literature against the charge of being a cor-
rupter of men on the very eve of the Elizabethan flower-
ing of the arts; and a succession of men and women went
to prison for selling Shelley's poems. The harsh pattern

of Swift's writing was fixed because he scandalized the religious sensibilities of Queen Anne. In our own day, Thomas Hardy, James Joyce, and D. H. Lawrence have been held to outrage and to undermine morality. Yet it is overwhelmingly likely that their books will survive when the thousand spruce and proper critics of the day have been forgotten.

Often the attack on a new outlook in the arts takes a slightly different ground. A book or a painting is held to be harmful to the public mind, by being not immoral but without morality at all. Raphael was criticized in this way for being amoral, and so were Whistler and the Pre-Raphaelites. In literature, Tolstoy's *Anna Karenina* was called amoral, with many other works of the Russian novelists and playwrights; and the list of English playwrights who have been charged with a lack of any moral sense goes all the way from the Restoration to Oscar Wilde and Bernard Shaw.

2

It is this last charge which is commonly brought against science. The claim is not that science is actively anti-moral, but that it is without morality of any kind. The implication is that it thereby breeds in the minds of those who practise it an indifference to morality which comes in time to atrophy in them the power of right judgement and the urge to good conduct.

This charge seems to me as false of the sciences as of the arts. No one who stops to think about *Anna Karenina* today believes that it is without morality, and that it makes no judgement on the complex actions of its heroine, her husband, and her lover. On the contrary, we find it a deeper and more moving book than a hundred conventional novels about that triangle, because it shows so much more patient, more understanding, and more heartbreaking an insight into the forces which buffet its men and women. It is not a conventional book, it is a true book. And we do not mean by truth some chance correspondence with the facts in a newspaper about a despairing woman who threw herself under a train. We mean that Tolstoy understood people and events, and saw within them the interplay of personality, passion, convention, and the impact on them of the to-and-fro of outside happenings. No ethic and no set of values has our respect now which does not recognize the truth in this.

There is indeed no system of morality which does not set a high value on truth and on knowledge, above all on a conscious knowledge of oneself. Is it therefore at least odd that science should be called amoral, and this by people who in their own lives set a high value on being truthful. For whatever else may be held against science, this cannot be denied, that it takes for ultimate judgement one criterion alone, that it shall be truthful. If there is one system which can claim a more fanatical regard for truth than Lao-tze and the Pilgrim Fathers, it is certainly science.

We cannot of course put their truth or any other human values quite so simply as this. We must look round and see whether, either in ethics or in science, truth does not extend beyond a simple truthfulness to fact. And we may take this inquiry into truth as a characteristic test for science, on which we can ground the larger decision, whether science does indeed possess its own values. But do not let us miss the simple point. Whatever else they have also meant by truth, men who take pride in their conduct and its underlying values do set store by truthfulness in the literal sense. They are ashamed to lie in fact and in intention. And this transcending respect for truthfulness is shared by science. T. H. Huxley was an agnostic, Clifford was an atheist, and I know at least one great mathematician who is a scoundrel. Yet all of them rest their scientific faith on an uncompromising adherence to the truth, and the irresistible urge to discover it. All of them spurn that grey appeal to expediency which is the withering thumbprint of the administrator in committee.

3

In the last thirty years, a school of philosophy has grown up which takes the narrow view, that to be true means to be verifiable in fact. It goes further and holds that no statement is meaningful if it cannot be put to the test of factual truth, at least in theory.

This test would limit our serious conversation to what the man in the street calls scientific matters, which can be defined and verified exactly. It rejects altogether such topics as value, ethics, and sentiments, claiming that discussion of them may be comforting and even entertaining, but is strictly without meaning. 'Virtue is its own reward' is in this philosophy a piece of meaningless good cheer; sensible philosophers only discuss such statements as 'Water is made up of hydrogen and oxygen'. Here we have a philosophy in which science seems to have gone over to the counter attack, by replying to the charge that it contains no values with the curt remark that values are a lot of nonsense anyway.

But as so often happens when philosophers take up arms for science, the science that is being defended is long out of date. The ideal of the meaningful and the true which this positivist philosophy sets up is indeed the nineteenth-century conception of science. These are the notions of meaning and of truth which Joule had in mind

5

a hundred years ago when he showed that heat is precisely a form of mechanical energy, or later Hertz when he found the radio waves whose existence had been implied by Clerk Maxwell's equations of the electromagnetic field. But such notions of truth have already turned out to be insufficient for science itself, in the modern sense. So that it is certainly an odd service to sweep value and ethics out of the door with this broom, which at once also gets rid of science and of human knowledge.

There are a number of grounds why logical positivism will not do; and they have this in common, that it is a piecemeal philosophy. It models itself on the heroic attempt by Russell and Whitehead to derive all mathematics, including such difficult ideas as the continuous and the infinite, from a finite number of axioms. Mathematics was to be built up step by step from a set of particulate or atomic propositions. This was a great and an important work in logic. It did not wholly succeed, even in its own field. But it remains a monument there to the two masters who created it.

The positivist philosophers have taken this attempt for their model, in picturing knowledge in the same way as built up from pieces of particulate fact. But if mathematics has difficulty in fitting this structure, it is plain that empirical knowledge does not begin to fit it. Obviously we do not get our knowledge in this way, from particulate pieces of information like 'this is red'. The mind does not begin from such sense experiences, but always from integrated bundles of them, that is from things. How else do I recognize what I am now looking at as a book, and identify it as the same book I was looking at before I turned the page? We do not make up our knowledge like a meccano set piecemeal from minute nuts and bolts of experience.

This in itself so far is only an issue of psychology. But there is a deeper issue, which is this, that neither can we break our experience down into these nuts and bolts. Not even as a hypothesis will it do to think of knowledge as reducible to atomic propositions.

I have already spoken of the logical reasons why this cannot be so. If it were, there would remain, in this atomic world of knowledge, statements which would be neither true nor false. So the logical positivist, having been at pains to call everything not in his meccano world nonsense, would discover that even this world is still chock-full of nonsense. But I do not want to stop at this logical failing, as if we were scoring debating points. What is the deeper reason why the atomic construction of knowledge fails? Why ought we to have foreseen that it must break down in contradiction?

The answer is that this atomic construction supposes, like the atomic science of the last century, that there lies below our experience a set of facts which are more exact than experience; which are indeed exact. 'This is red,' we are told, and it is assumed that we have now dug down to a base of knowledge where there is no more room for disagreement: either this is red, or it is not red. But what is 'this' that we are both supposed, the speaker and I, to see as the same spot? And what is the red about which as sensible beings we cannot differ? Red light has a wavelength of about one three-hundred-thousandth of an inch: to what order of accuracy are we to read it in order to agree on our atomic proposition?

In the world of science, neither 'this' nor 'red' are entities which can be defined with complete precision. 'This' will always escape in the Brownian to-and-fro of atoms, and 'red' must be embedded in a range of uncertainty of a few wavelengths. The world cannot be described, as positivists have explicitly supposed, by giving exact physical co-ordinates to every point in a statement, and then verifying whether or not the statement is true. Every co-ordinate reference must carry with it an area of uncertainty. And this implies that the verification is itself uncertain, and must be allowed a margin of error. To think otherwise is to wish oneself back to the atomic paradise of a hundred and fifty years ago, and to the blissful simplicity of which Blake said with imaginative contempt that it hoped 'to build a Universe with Farthing Balls'.

It is indeed clear that there is an essential fault within the basic conception of the positivist, that we can judge truth by a simple act of verification. What are we to verify? An atomic proposition, that is a statement in the simplest form about the simplest kind of fact. But the facts do not keep still for us, either in space or in time. I cannot verify now a statement about a fact which has already passed. I must make my statement about a future fact, and this means that I must turn it into a prediction. Indeed, the idea of verification must imply prediction, and prediction as we have seen cannot be separated from its own area of uncertainty.

4

What I have written is not meant to belittle nineteenth-century science. By no means; it was a wonderful achievement, and the bulk of it remains so to this day. But there runs under it a conception of the world which has turned out to be too simple. The conception was of a world which could be described exactly, if not by today's scientists then by tomorrow's. I learned to think about that world from the lively account of a master of simple exposition, the geometer and philosopher William Clifford. His account was called characteristically *The*

Common Sense of the Exact Sciences. The difference between his title and mine is not accidental. I have deliberately chosen the title *The Common Sense of Science* because it underlines the difference between our two centuries. We see today that in the strict sense there are no exact sciences. There is science, and there is common sense; and both must learn to assimilate into their methods and basic ideas the underlying uncertainties of all knowledge.

The best scientists of the last century did foresee this. I have spoken of Clifford, and it is fair to the memory of that great man to recall that he had some of this foresight. Indeed, Clifford had a genius for such prophetic insight. *The Common Sense of the Exact Sciences* contains the first hint of the idea that massive bodies give a local curvature to space, which Einstein has since worked out fully. Clifford was after all a contemporary of Galton, and when he died at thirty-five his book was edited by the founder of modern statistics, Karl Pearson. And here is what Clifford said about scientific truth, looking out of the nineteenth century forward into ours.

Remember, then, that scientific thought is the guide of action; that the truth at which it arrives is not that which we can ideally contemplate without error, but that which we may act upon without fear; and you cannot fail to see that scientific thought is not an accompaniment or condition of human progress, but human progress itself.

This is an arresting thought on a number of counts. It puts pithily the view of science as action which I have underlined. And the action looks forward; it is distinguished from contemplation by looking towards the future. And arresting too here is the criterion of what is true. The realistic basis of science as I have stressed it cannot be put better than in Clifford's definition, that its truth 'is not that which we can ideally contemplate without error, but that which we may act upon without fear.'

What science observes, what science predicts has all the shortcomings of fact. The facts supply the signal for the future, but the signal is necessarily uncertain and its interpretation against the background of the irrelevant will be inaccurate. The prediction which we base on the signal must be a statistical one. It does not read the future, it forecasts it; and the forecast has meaning only because we couple it with its own estimate of uncertainty. The future is as it were always a little out of focus, and everything that we foresee in it is seen embedded in a small area of uncertainty. It is the human situation and the situation of science. We do not contemplate the facts without error, but because we know what we are doing, we may act upon them without fear.

'Because we know what we are doing': this is the crux of science. We are not merely observing and predicting facts; and that is why any philosophy which builds up science only from facts is mistaken. We know, that is we find laws; and every human action uses these laws, and at the same time tests them and feels towards new laws. It is not the form of these laws which matters. The laws of science, like those which we use in our private behaviour, remain helpful and truthful whether they contain words like 'always', or only 'more often than not'. What matters is the recognition of the law in the facts. It is the law which we verify: the pattern, the order, the structure of events. This is why science is so full of the symbolism of numbers and geometry, which are the most familiar expressions of structural relations.

5

There is no sense at all in which science can be called a mere description of facts. It is in no sense, as humanists sometimes pretend, a neutral record of what happens in an endless mechanical encyclopedia. This mistaken view goes back to the eighteenth century. It pictures scientists as utilitarians still crying *Let be!* and still believing that the world runs best with no other regulating principles than natural gravitation and human self-interest.

But this picture of the world of Mandeville and Bentham and Dickens's *Hard Times* was never science. For science is not the blank record of facts, but the search for order within the facts. And the truth of science is not truth to fact, which can never be more than approximate, but the truth of the laws which we see within the facts. And this kind of truth is as difficult and as human as the sense of truth in a painting which is not a photograph, or the feeling of emotional truth in a movement in music. When we speak of truth, we make a judgement between what matters and what does not, and we feel the unity of its different parts. We do this as much in science as in the arts or in daily life. We make a judgement when we prefer one theory to another even in science, since there is always an endless number of theories which can account for all the known facts. And the principles of this judgement have some deep appeal which is more than merely factual. William of Ockham first suggested to scientists that they should prefer that theory which uses in its explanation the smallest number of unknown agents. Science has held to this principle now for six hundred years. But is there indeed any ground for it other than a kind of aesthetic satisfaction, much like that of sacrificing your queen at chess in order to mate with a knight?

We cannot define truth in science until we move from fact to law. And within the body of laws in turn, what impresses us as truth is the orderly coherence of the pieces. They fit together like the characters in a great novel, or like the words in a poem. Indeed, we should keep that last analogy by us always. For science is a language, and like a language, it defines its parts by the way they make up a meaning. Every word in the sentence has some uncertainty of definition, and yet the sentence defines its own meaning and that of its words conclusively. It is the internal unity and coherence of science which give it truth, and which make it a better system of prediction than any less orderly language.

6

I have singled out truth among the human values for this reason. It is common to all systems of value, and is fundamental to most of them. And it is a value. We cannot take it for granted as something self-evident in science any more than in art or morals or religion. In all of them truth rests on an act of free human judgement. In none of them of course can this judgement be exercised without experience: there is no truth, not even religious truth, which calls for no sanction from fact. There are other values: goodness, beauty, right conduct. They have their echoes even in science; and there is one value, freedom of human ideas, which is the essential condition for the health of science. But it is not my point to show laboriously that science as much as the arts creates and implies all the human values. I have wanted to show only in one example that science cannot exist without judgements of value. This example, the truth, is a critical one; and it will serve to show that science cannot exist as a blank and mechanical activity.

There is still more in science than this. It shares the values of all human action, and it also adds to these values. The human values penetrate through all our actions, and they are strikingly alike in civilizations which are thousands of years apart. The Aztecs and the Minoans, the Chaldees, the Cherokees, and the Shakers held in common ideas about human dignity and value which go far deeper than the surface differences of time and place. The likenesses are as heartening in their arts and their speculations. Yet, though the values are alike, they are not identical. The human values change, slowly but not negligibly. And in this change, science plays a creative part.

For the values rest at bottom on acts of judgement. And every act of judgement is a division of the field of our experience into what matters and what does not. I spoke of this at the beginning of this book: that at the basis of human thought lies the judgement of what is like and what is unlike. In picking out what we shall call alike, we make the basic judgement, that here is something which is important to us. We do this when we say that men are like women, or that the earth is like the planets, or that the air is like wine. Aldous Huxley in his novel *Barren Leaves* speculates at length about the word 'love' in different European languages; but I, coming to England as a boy, was struck more by the existence in English alone of the verb 'to like'.

The human values are bound up with what we judge to be like and unlike; and when science shifts that judgement, it makes as profound a shift in these values. The Greeks built a wonderful civilization, yet it did not outrage their sense of values to hold men in slavery. They did not feel the slave and citizen to be alike men. By the end of the eighteenth century, it was felt in the western world that all white men are alike; but William Wilberforce spent a lifetime in persuading his generation that black slaves and white are alike in human dignity. Science helped to create that sensibility, by widening the view of what is like and what unlike. It helped to widen it enough to make cruelty to animals a particularly detested offence in England. In our own generation, we have seen the human values perverted in Nazi Germany into a monstrous scale of self-approval. And the perversion was bolstered by a deliberate attempt to go back on what science and humanity had struggled slowly to grasp, the likeness of man. The hateful values of the Nazi rest at bottom on this false judgement, which science for three hundred years has tried to root out: that what I do is not like what others do.

7

This is the constant urge of science as well as of the arts, to broaden the likeness for which we grope under the facts. When we discover the wider likeness, whether between space and time, or between the bacillus, the virus, and the crystal, we enlarge the order in the universe; but more than this, we enlarge its unity. And it is the unity of nature, living and dead, for which our thought reaches. This is a far deeper conception than any assumption that nature must be uniform. We seek to find nature one, a coherent unity. This gives to scientists their sense of mission and, let us acknowledge it, of aesthetic fulfilment: that every research carries the sense of drawing together the threads of the world into a patterned web.

Each law of science so holds together a scattered array of facts. But the laws themselves are not the final unifying agents. Each law is still only a rule for making predictions, as Aristotle predicted that apples will go on falling

to the ground. The great unifying thoughts are knots
where the laws cross one another and are held together:
the thought that all matter is alike, or that earthly space
runs beyond the stars, or that there is a physical conti-
nuity from one generation to the next. We come to take
these crossing places for granted, and forget how long it
took to make these concepts. Yet it is they that give the
unity: the concept of matter, of space, of evolution and
inheritance. They are the links and the critical joints in
the whole structure of our understanding. And they are
not self-evident: mass, energy, mind, the nervous system,
the ecology of host and enzyme: these were not obvious
to Aquinas and ready to be shuffled into laws by the
first gifted mathematician. On the contrary, just as the
laws unite the facts, so the concepts of science unite its
laws into an orderly world which hangs on those bold
knots in the network.

When we follow the growth of a science, we come to
understand how that movement has been probing for
these unifying concepts. Look at the movement of biology since the day of Ray and Linnaeus: the listing of
like species, the discovery of cells, of their division and of
their sexual fusion; the elaboration of the mechanisms of
inheritance and of natural selection; and from all these,
the long distillation of the rich and many-sided concept
of evolution. Look at chemistry, from Dalton's law of the
combination of constant weights through the periodic
table of the elements and the work of Davy and Faraday
on their electric behaviour, to the complex concepts of
molecular structure today and of the more and the less
saturated shells of electrons in the chemical atom. Or
look at the march of physics to unity: the slow crystalliza-
tion in the Scientific Revolution of the universal concepts of matter, mass, and weight; the concept of the conservation of mass, the concept of energy in its many

forms, in Rumford and Joule and Clerk Maxwell, and
of its conservation; the leap by Planck in 1900 to the
particulate nature of energy; and then the most brilliant
piece of unifying insight, Einstein's identification of mass
and energy in a single concept. We have seen this lead to
the creation of energy from matter; to a picture of space
as closed but possibly expanding; and now, in the last
years, to the speculation that in the process of expansion,
gravitational energy is indirectly lost, and may reappear
as new-born matter. Science is a process of creating new
concepts which unify our understanding of the world,
and the process is today bolder and more far-reaching,
more triumphant even than at the great threshold of the
Scientific Revolution.

8

The concepts of value are not different in kind from
these. It is not easy to formulate laws of art; at least, as
the Augustans showed so woefully, the laws which are
easy to formulate are bad laws. Yet there is a likeness
which runs under all works of art, and the single works
are held together by common standards. And the standards in turn are unified in such larger concepts, such
knots which hold the different historical tastes together,
as the concepts of beauty and truth and coherence. So
the rules of conduct run together at last in the concepts of
truth and goodness and justice and right and duty. These
concepts of value are not the same as the concepts of
science. But like them they express the deep relation between the human mind and the world which it matches.
If this were a book about aesthetics, I should have studied
the way in which concepts like taste and fitness and
beauty have grown and how they cohere together. And
if this were a book about ethics, I should have studied
another range of concepts of value. In a book about

science, I have looked at the growth of its concepts: the machine and the model, order, cause and chance, prediction and the future, the fundamental concept of law and the particular concepts which range from waves to matter and the cell. All these are expressions of the relation of man and his societies to the universal nature. None is achieved without man's judgement of that order, what is like and what is unlike, what in it matters and what does not. Let us not forget this judgement even in the humblest law about ohms and volts and ampères, for it rests at bottom on a choice of something that man feels to bind him to his environment. The judgement is already in the work. The work of art contains the artist's judgement; so that it has been wisely said of it, that it is not we by our standards who judge the work of art, but the work which judges us. And in the same sense, it is not we who stand perplexed round the discoveries of science who judge it, but science which judges us. Einstein rounded out three centuries of questioning of nature when he equated energy and mass in a single line,

$$E = mc^2.$$

This is not the same unification of concepts as that for which Keats was searching when he closed the *Ode on a Grecian Urn* with the lines,

> *Beauty is truth, truth beauty, – that is all*
> *Ye know on earth, and all ye need to know.*

But the likeness is more important than the difference. The likeness is more helpful in making us understand that the concepts of science are like the concepts of value, monuments to our sense of unity in nature.

CHAPTER 9

Science, the Destroyer or Creator

I

WE all know the story of the sorcerer's apprentice; or *Frankenstein* which Mary Shelley wrote in competition with her husband and Byron; or some other story of the same kind out of the macabre invention of the nineteenth century. In these stories, someone who has special powers over nature conjures or creates a stick or a machine to do his work for him; and then finds that he cannot take back the life he has given it. The mindless monster overwhelms him; and what began as an invention to do the housework ends by destroying the master with the house.

These stories have become the epitome of our own fears. We have been inventing machines at a growing pace now for about three hundred years. This is a short span even in our recorded history, and it is not a thousandth part of our history as men. In that short moment of time we have found a remarkable insight into the workings of nature. We have used it to make ourselves far more flexible in our adaptation to the outside world than any other animal has ever been. We can survive in climates which even germs find difficult. We can grow our own food and meat. We can travel overland and we can tunnel and swim and fly, all in the one body. More important than any of these, we have come nearest to the dream which Lamarck had, that animals might inherit the skills which their parents learned. We have discovered the means to record our experience so that others may live it again.

The history of other animal species shows that the

most successful in the struggle for survival have been those which were most adaptable to changes in their world. We have made ourselves by means of our tools beyond all measure more adaptable than any other species, living or extinct; and we continue to do so with gathering speed. Yet today we are afraid of our own shadow in the nine o'clock news; and we wonder whether we shall survive so over-specialized a creature as the Pekinese.

2

Every one likes to blame his sense of defeat on someone else; and for some time scientists have been a favourite scapegoat. I want to look at their responsibility, and for that matter at everybody's, rather more closely. They do have a special responsibility; do not let us argue that out of existence; but it is a complicated one, and it is not the whole responsibility. For example, science obviously is not responsible for the readiness of people, who do not take their private quarrels beyond the stage of insult, to carry their public quarrels to the point of war. Many animals fight for their needs, and some for their mere greeds, to the point of death. Bucks fight for females, and birds fight for their territories. The fighting habits of man are odd because he displays them only in groups. But they were not supplied by scientists. On the contrary, science has helped to end several kinds of group murder, such as witch hunting and the taboos of the early nineteenth century against disinfecting hospitals.

Neither is science responsible for the existence of groups which believe themselves to be in competition: for the existence above all of nations. And the threat of war today is always a national threat. Some bone of contention and competition is identified with a national need: Fiume or the Polish corridor or the dignity of the

Austrian Empire; and in the end nations are willing to organize and to invite the death of citizens on both sides in order to reach these collective aims. Science did not create the nations; on the contrary, it has helped to soften those strong national idiosyncrasies which it seems necessary to exploit if war is to be made with enthusiasm. And wars are not made by *any* traditional groups: they are made by highly organized societies, they are made by nations. Most of us have seen Yorkshiremen invade Old Trafford, and a bloody nose or two if the day was thirsty. But no Yorkshireman would have grown pale if he had been told that Lancashire had the atomic bomb.

The sense of doom in us today is not a fear of science; it is a fear of war. And the causes of war were not created by science; they do not differ in kind from the known causes of the War of Jenkins' Ear or the Wars of the Roses, which were carried on with only the most modest scientific aids. No, science has not invented war; but it has turned it into a very different thing. The people who distrust it are not wrong. The man in the pub who says 'It'll wipe out the world', the woman in the queue who says 'It isn't natural' – they do not express themselves very well; but what they are trying to say does make sense. Science has enlarged the mechanism of war, and it has distorted it. It has done this in at least two ways.

3

First, science has obviously multiplied the power of the war-makers. The weapons of the moment can kill more people more secretly and more unpleasantly than those of the past. This progress – as for want of another word I must call it – this progress has been going on for some time; and for some time it has been said, of each new weapon, that it is so destructive or so horrible that it will frighten people into their wits, and force the nations to give up war for lack of cannon fodder. This hope has never been fulfilled, and I know no one who takes refuge in it today. The acts of men and women are not dictated by such simple compulsions; and they themselves do not stand in any simple relation to the decisions of the nations which they compose. Grapeshot and TNT and gas have not helped to outlaw war; and I see no sign that the hydrogen bomb or a whiff of bacteria will be more successful in making men wise by compulsion.

Secondly, science at the same time has given the nations quite new occasions for falling out. I do not mean such simple objectives as someone else's uranium mine, or a Pacific Island which happens to be knee-deep in organic fertilizer. I do not even mean merely another nation's factories and her skilled production. These are all parts of the surplus above our simple needs which they themselves help to create and which gives our civilization its character. And war in our world battens on this surplus. This is the object of the greed of nations, and this also gives them the leisure to train and the means to arm for war. At bottom, we have remained individually too greedy to distribute our surplus, and collectively too stupid to pile it up in any more useful form than the traditional mountains of arms. Science can claim to have created the surplus in our societies, and we know from the working day and the working diet how greatly it has increased it in the last two hundred years. Science has created the surplus. Now put this year's budget beside the budget of 1750, anywhere in the world, and you will see what we are doing with it.

I myself think there is a third dimension which science has added to modern war. It has created war nerves and the war of nerves. I am not thinking about the technical conditions for a war of nerves: the camera man and the radio and the massed display of strength. I am thinking of the climate in which this stage lightning flickers and is made to seem real. The last thirty years have given us a frightening show of these mental states. There is a division in the mind of each of us, that has become plain, between the man and the brute; and the rift can be opened, the man submerged, with a cynical simplicity, with the meanest tools of envy and frustration, which in my boyhood would have been thought inconceivable in a civilized society. I shall come back to this cleavage in our minds, for it is much more than an item in a list of war crimes. But it is an item. It helps to create the conditions for disaster. And I think that science has contributed to it. Science; the fact that science is there, mysterious, powerful; the fact that most people are impressed by it but ignorant and helpless – all this seems to me to have contributed to the division in our minds. And scientists cannot escape the responsibility for this. They have enjoyed acting the mysterious stranger, the powerful voice without emotion, the expert and the god. They have failed to make themselves comfortable in the talk of people in the street; no one taught them the knack, of course, but they were not keen to learn. And now they find the distance which they enjoyed has turned to distrust, and the awe has turned to fear; and people who are by no means fools really believe that we should be better off without science.

4

These are the indictments which scientists cannot escape. Of course, they are often badly phrased, so that scientists can side-step them with generalities about the common responsibility, and who voted the credits for atomic research anyway; which are perfectly just, but not at all relevant. That is not the heart of the matter; and the people in queues and pubs are humbly groping for the heart. They are not good at saying things and they do not give model answers to interviewers. But when they say 'We've forgotten what's right,' when they say 'We're not fit to handle such things,' what is in their minds is perfectly true. Science and society are out of joint. Science has given to no one in particular a power which no one in particular knows how to use. Why do not scientists invent something sensible? Wives say it every time they stub their toe on the waste bin, and husbands say it whenever a fuse blows. Why is it the business of no one in particular to stop fitting science for death and to begin fitting it into our lives? We will agree that warlike science is no more than a by-product of a warlike society. Science has merely provided the means, for good or for ill; and society has seized it for ill. But what are we going to do about it?

The first thing to do, it seems to me, is to treat this as a scientific question: by which I mean as a practical and sensible question, which deserves a factual approach and a reasoned answer. Now that I have apologized on behalf of scientists, and this on a scale which some of them will certainly think too ample, let us cut out what usually happens to the argument at this point, the rush of re-criminations. The scientists are conscious of their mistakes; and I do not want to discuss the mistakes of non-scientists – although they have made a great many – except those which we all must begin to make good.

I have said that a scientific answer must be practical as well as sensible. This really rules out at once the panaceas which also tend to run the argument into a blind alley at this stage; the panaceas which say summarily 'Get rid of them.' Naturally, it does not seem to me to be sensible to get rid of scientists; but in any case, it plainly is not practical. And whatever we do with our own scientists, it very plainly is not practical to get rid of the scientists of rival nations; because if there existed the conditions for agreement among nations on this far-reaching scheme, then the conditions for war would already have disappeared. If there existed the conditions for international agreement, say to suspend all scientific research, or to abandon warlike research, or in any other way to forgo science as an instrument of nationalism – if such agreements could be reached, then they would already be superfluous; because the conditions for war would already have disappeared. So, however we might sigh for Samuel Butler's panacea in *Erewhon*, simply to give up all machines, there is no point in talking about it. I believe it would be a disaster for mankind like the coming of the Dark Ages. But there is no point in arguing this. It just is not practical, nationally or internationally.

There are no panaceas at all; and we had better face that. There is nothing that we can do overnight, in a week or a month, which can straighten by a laying on of hands the ancient distortion of our society. Do not let us fancy that any one of us out of the blue will concoct that stirring letter to *The Times* which will change the black mood of history – and the instructions to diplomats. Putting scientists in the Cabinet will not do that, and women in the War Office will not, nor will bishops in the Privy Council. There are no panaceas. We are the heirs to a tradition which has left science and society out of step. The man in the street is right: we have never learned to handle such things. Nothing will do but that we learn. But learning is not done in a year. Our ultimate survival is in our own hands. Our survival while we are learning is a much chancier thing. We had better be realistic about that.

Meanwhile we had better settle down to work for our ultimate survival; and we had better start now. We have seen that the diagnosis has turned out to be not very difficult. Science and our social habits are out of step. And the cure is no deeper either. We must learn to match them. And there is no way of learning this unless we learn to understand *both*.

5

Of the two, of course, the one which is strange is science. I have already blamed the scientist for that. He has been the monk of our age, timid, thwarted, anxious to be asked to help; and with a secret ambition to play the Grey Eminence. Through years of childhood poverty he dreamed of this. Scientific skill was a blue door beckoning to him, which would open into the society of dignitaries of state. But the private motives of scientists are not the trend of science. The trend of science is made by the needs of society: navigation before the eighteenth century, manufacture thereafter; and in our age I believe the liberation of personality. Whatever the part which scientists like to act, or for that matter which painters like to dress, science shares the aims of our society just as art does. The difficulties of understanding either are not fundamental; they are difficulties only of language. To grow familiar with the large ideas of science calls for patience and an effort of attention; and I hope I have shown that it repays them.

For two hundred years, these ideas have been applied to technical needs; and they have made our world anew, triumphantly, from top to toe. Our shoes are tanned and stitched, our clothes are spun and dyed and woven, we are lighted and carried and doctored by means which were unknown to neat Mr Pope at Twickenham in 1740. We may not think that is much to put against the eighty thousand dead in Hiroshima, or we may. We may not think it recompenses us for the absence of any Mr Pope from Twickenham today; we may even hold it responsible. It is certainly not a spiritual achievement. But it has not yet tried to be. It has applied its ideas monotonously to shoe-leather and bicycle bells. And it has made a superb job of them. Compare its record in its own field with that of any other ideas of the same age: Burke's ideas of the imagination, or Bentham's on government, or Adam Smith on political economy. If any ideas have a claim to be called creative, because they have created something, then certainly it is the ideas of science.

We may think that all that science has created is comfort; and it certainly has done that – the very word 'comfortable' in the modern sense dates from the Industrial Revolution. But have we always stopped to think what science has done not to our mode of living but to our life? We talk about research for death, the threat of war and the number of civilians who get killed. But have we always weighed this against the increase in our own life span? Let us do a small sum. The number of people killed in Great Britain in six years of war by German bombs, flying bombs, and V2s was sixty thousand. They were an average lot of people, which means that on an average they lost half their expectation of life. Quite an easy long division shows that the effect of this in our population of fifty million people was to shorten the average span of life by less than one tenth of one per cent. This is about a fortnight. Put this on the debit side. And on the credit side, we know that in the last hundred years the average span of life in England has increased by twenty years. That is the price of science, take it or leave it – a fortnight for twenty years of life. And these twenty years have been created by applying to daily life, to clothing and bedding, to hygiene and infection, to birth and death, the simple ideas of science – the fundamental ideas I have been talking about: order, cause, and chance. If any ideas have a claim to be called creative, because they have created life, it is the ideas of science.

6

We have not neglected these ideas altogether in our social organization. But, it is a point I have made several times, we have got hopelessly behind with them. The idea of order is now old enough to have reached at least our filing cabinets. The idea of cause and effect has entered our habits, until it has become the new *a priori* in the making of administrative plans. The difficulty is to dislodge it, now that it is hardening into a scholastic formula. For the idea which has given a new vigour to science in our generation is larger than the machinery of cause and effect. It stipulates no special mechanism between the present and the future. It is content to predict the future, without insisting that the computation must follow the steps of causal law. I have called this the idea of chance, because its method is statistical, and because it recognizes that every prediction carries with it its own measurable uncertainty. A good prediction is one which defines its area of uncertainty; a bad prediction ignores it. And at bottom this is no more than the return to the essentially empirical, the experimental nature of science. Science is a great many things, and I have called them a great many names; but in the end they all return to this: science is the acceptance of what works and the rejection of what does not. That needs more courage than we might think.

It needs more courage than we have ever found when we have faced our worldly problems. This is how society has lost touch with science: because it has hesitated to judge itself by the same impersonal code of what works and what does not. We have clung to Adam Smith and Burke, or we have agitated for Plato and Aquinas, through wars and famine, through rising and falling birth-rates, and through libraries of learned argument. And in the end, our eyes have always wandered from the birth-rate to the argument: from the birth-rate to what we have wanted to believe. Here is the crux of what I have been saying. Here is our ultimate hope of saving ourselves from extinction. We must learn to understand that the content of all knowledge is empirical; that its test is whether it works; and we must learn to act on that understanding in the world as well as in the laboratory.

This is the message of science: our ideas must be realistic, flexible, unbigoted – they must be human, they must create their own authority. If any ideas have a claim to be called creative, because they have liberated that creative impulse, it is the ideas of science.

7

This is not only a material code. On the contrary, my hope is that it may heal the spiritual cleft which two wars have uncovered. I have seen in my lifetime an abyss open in the human mind: a gulf between the endeavour to be man, and the relish in being brute. The scientist has indeed had a hand in this, and every other specialist too, with his prim detachment and his oracular airs. But of course, the large strain which has opened this fault is social. We have made men live in two halves, a Sunday half and a workday one. We have ordered them to love their neighbour and to turn the other cheek, in a society which has constantly compelled them to shoulder their neighbour aside and to turn their backs. So we have created a savage sense of failure which, as we know now to our cost, can be tapped with an ease which is frightening; and which can thrust up, with explosive force, a symbol to repeat to an unhappy people its most degrading dream.

Can science heal that neurotic flaw in us? If science cannot, then nothing can. Let us stop pretending. There is no cure in high moral precepts. We have preached them too long to men who are forced to live how they can: *that* makes the strain which they have not been able to bear. We need an ethic which is moral *and* which works. It is often said that science has destroyed our values and put nothing in their place. What has really happened of course is that science has shown in harsh relief the division between our values and our world. We have not begun to let science get into our heads; where then was it supposed to create these values? We have used it as a machine without will, the conjured spirit to do the chores. I believe that science can create values; and will create them precisely as literature does, by looking into the human personality; by discovering what divides it and what cements it. That is how great writers have explored man, and this whether they themselves as men have been driven by the anguish in *Gulliver's Travels* or the sympathy in *Moll Flanders*. The insight of science is not different from that of the arts. Science will create values, I believe, and discover virtues, when it looks into man; when it explores what makes him man and not an animal, and what makes his societies human and not animal packs.

I believe that we can reach this unity in our culture. I began this book by recalling that nations in their great ages have not been great in art or science, but in art and science. Rembrandt was the contemporary of Huygens and Spinoza. At that very time, Isaac Newton walked with Dryden and Christopher Wren. We know that ours is a remarkable age of science. It is for us to use it to broaden and to liberate our culture. These are the marks of science: that it is open for all to hear, and all are free to speak their minds in it. They are marks of the world at its best, and the human spirit at its most challenging.

Index

Published and distributed by
TOBAR LIMITED
The Old Aerodrome, Worlingham, Beccles,
Suffolk, NR34 7SP, UK

www.tobar.co.uk

This edition printed 2009

© 2009 Arcturus Publishing Limited

Printed in China

ISBN 13: 978-1-903230-33-6
AD001151EN

Cover: David Mostyn

CONTENTS

INTRODUCTION

The final curtain awaits us all; it's one of the few certainties in life, but it should be the very least of your concerns. You should just hope that when it does come to checking-out time, you manage to go with dignity and decorum – and without people laughing at how you shuffled off this mortal coil. After all, you wouldn't want to go out like many of the people featured in this book.

From bizarre murders and strange suicides through to life-extinguishing affairs of the heart, humankind appears to be just as determined to leave its mark on death as on life. And all the while, the Grim Reaper can be heard faintly chuckling in the background.

So sit back, read these pages – and then pray that you don't find yourself in the sequel. We'll be watching…

Absolutely Tragic

So outlandish are the circumstances surrounding certain deaths that the whole thing can seem like a fabrication: an urban myth spun across the Internet that's taken on a life of its own. The following events really did happen, though. There are some truly tragic examples of people who have received a sudden final slap from the cruel hand of Lady Luck through no fault of their own, but other demises were brought about by the victims' own stupidity – they seemed to be really asking for it. Tragedy, it would seem, can strike anywhere and at any time. But forewarned is forearmed – if you are going to rob a bank, try to make it out of there before the time bomb strapped to your neck goes off…

Keeping It In The Family

They say bad luck comes in threes, but in the case of one Thai family in the early 1990s twice proved more than enough. Yooket Paen, a 57-year-old woman, was making her way across a field on her farm when she lost her footing in the mud. As Paen fell, she tried to grab on to something to break her fall. Her hand unfortunately latched on to an exposed electrical wire which instantly electrocuted her. This story would be sad enough – and would have Health & Safety types nodding their heads sagely – but tragedy struck again when her sister, Yooket Pan, was showing neighbours where the tragic accident had happened. She inadvertently slipped and history repeated itself as she grabbed the very same wire and was killed on the very same spot.

Ridicule Mortis
Moldova in Europe has the highest rate of death caused by lawnmowers in the world.

PLANE UNLUCKY

It's perhaps the most extreme example of plane bad luck on record. Russian fighter pilot, Nikolai Skurigin, ejected from his plane over Poland because he believed that the MiG-23's engine was about to fail. As it turns out, he was wrong because the plane continued flying on autopilot across western Europe to Belgium where it finally ran out of fuel after 560 miles and crashed into a farmhouse, killing the 18-year-old man inside…

Roadkill

People are always in a hurry to get to work – and none more so than the commuters of San Francisco. Police began receiving reports of a dead animal on Interstate 880 but when they arrived at the scene it was not some poor mutt ground into the highway but a human ear. Further investigation revealed the body parts of a man scattered across five lanes – his bits and pieces covered 1,000 feet of highway. It would seem that the man (of an indeterminable age) had been hit and then hit several times more in the early hours of the morning. To underline this, police received 80 phone calls from distressed drivers about the blood and guts they had found on their metalwork at the end of their journeys.

8

Lightning Strikes Twice

Or dental tools can, at least. Take Charles Gaal who in 2006 visited his local dentist, Dr Wesley Meyers, who had been practising dentistry for 35 years. The procedure was to replace Gaal's lower dentures – sadly, during the operation, the dentist managed to drop a small surgical screwdriver down Gaal's throat, which required surgery to remove. Fast-forward six months and you'd have thought that the dentist would take extra care when Gaal reappeared in his chair. Alas, it was not to be – this time, Dr Meyers accidentally dropped a surgical wrench down the poor man's throat. Even worse however, the one-inch instrument ended up in Gaal's lung and the Second World War veteran died two months later from complications brought about by this unwelcome intrusion.

Tales Of The Macabre

In the US a female murder victim's body was hard to identify because her head was missing. Thankfully, investigators were able to find out who she was by checking the serial numbers on her breast and bottom implants.

Forgive & Forget

Imagine you're a parent and you hear that the best friend of your son has managed to decapitate your loved one. How? By driving home drunk late one evening in 2004 and letting said best buddy lean out of the window before striking a telegraph pole, resulting in his head being removed from its shoulders. Now imagine that the driver carried on home with your son's headless body in the passenger seat. On arrival, the drunk driver then left the body in the car for neighbours to find and went to bed to sleep off the booze. Such a gruelling situation actually happened to the Brohm family in Marietta, Georgia, USA. You would have thought they would be angry and out for justice – but no, they made a plea for the inadvertent killer of their son to be released from jail so he could begin 'healing'…

Say Cheese...

If you find yourself lying on a Kansas convenience shop floor after being stabbed, remember to smile for the camera before you gulp your last breath. In 2007, five shoppers stepped over innocent shopper, LaShanda Calloway, who'd been stabbed during a robbery at a Kansas store and was bleeding to death; one of the shoppers paused briefly to take a picture of the poor woman on their mobile. Calloway later died from her injuries.

'The fact that people were more interested in taking a picture with a cell phone and shopping for snacks rather than helping this innocent young woman is, frankly, revolting.'– A Kansas police spokesperson to Fox News

Bad Call

Here in the West, we deal with our incompetent managers and executives with a bit of bad press, an insistence that they make a public apology and a huge pension payout once the dust settles. Yes, we are suckers. In North Korea however, they take managers' irresponsibility more seriously. A factory boss was found guilty of making personal international phone calls from his company and was executed by firing squad in front of 150,000 people. Worse still, six people were crushed to death as the crowds left to go home.

The Final Upgrade

Paying through the nose to fly first class should grant you such privileges as decent food, a complimentary glass or three of wine and, most importantly, the right not to wake up to find a corpse sitting next to you. But first-class flyer Paul Trinder may be considering swimming from India to Britain next time instead of using a well-known British airline. After all, he awoke to find the dead body of a frail woman, who had passed away during the flight, in the seat right next to him. Officials said that economy class was full at the time so the first class cabin was the best place for her. Perhaps somebody should have warned Trinder about her unexpected upgrade…

According to stats, around 10 UK passengers die on BA flights each year.

Hit-ching A Lift!

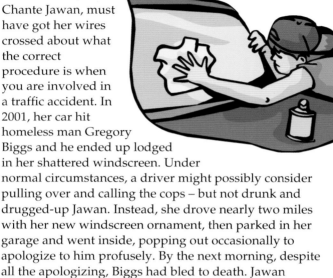

A former Texan nurse aide, Chante Jawan, must have got her wires crossed about what the correct procedure is when you are involved in a traffic accident. In 2001, her car hit homeless man Gregory Biggs and he ended up lodged in her shattered windscreen. Under normal circumstances, a driver might possibly consider pulling over and calling the cops – but not drunk and drugged-up Jawan. Instead, she drove nearly two miles with her new windscreen ornament, then parked in her garage and went inside, popping out occasionally to apologize to him profusely. By the next morning, despite all the apologizing, Biggs had bled to death. Jawan received a 50-year prison sentence.

A Harsh Reality

In 1998, a French woman became so distracted trying to save a virtual life that she ended up taking a real one. While driving her car, the woman's Tamagotchi, a Japanese virtual pet usually kept on a keyring, started bleeping because it needed urgent attention. As she tried to sort out its distressed calls, she ploughed into a group of cyclists, killing one.

Famous Last Words
'I am about to – or I am going to – die. Either expression is correct.' – *Dominique Bouhours, the famous French grammarian*

Road Rabid

After a near-accident on a quiet country road in the Cotswolds, Serena Sutton-Smith was so angry that she went on to ram the back of the car she had nearly run into. Overcome with rage, Sutton-Smith sat there with her foot pressed down on the accelerator, her car's wheels spinning so much that the tyre rubber sheared off, leaving the metal rims of the wheels scraping the road. The ensuing mass of sparks then set her engine on fire. Despite the efforts of concerned bystanders, who tried to convince Sutton-Smith to get out of her burning Vauxhall Nova, she was so furious that she simply sat tight, revving her engine, spinning the wheels and swearing her head off until she burnt to death.

Thick as Thieves

Being thick seems to be a must-have attribute for many a criminal – perhaps none more so than Italian Andreas Plack, a 23-year-old who in 2001 thought that he and his cousin, Christian Kleon, could defraud insurance companies by hacking off his leg, thus claiming thousands and thousands of Euros for the permanent disability. To aid their claim, the two cousins intended to say that Plack had been the victim of a ferocious mugging. The plan, though, came off the rails when Kleon cut through his cousin's leg below the knee with a power saw and managed to slice through a main artery. Plack bled to death before he could make an emergency phone call to save his own life. Claim cancelled.

Ridicule Mortis

Pity the poor Iranian hunter who thought holding the head of a snake down with his rifle butt would help him catch it – sadly though, the snake wrapped itself round the trigger of the loaded gun, pulled it and killed the hunter instead. Talk about the scales of justice.

14

Fast Food

It's the things you love the most that kill you. It's something that Mexican chef Juan Ruiz must have taken to heart quite literally when an uncooked strand of spaghetti was lifted and hurled through the air by a 150mph wind that swept through his restaurant. Said 'shard' managed to puncture Ruiz's chest and slice through his heart, killing him.

Time Out

Pizza delivery man Brian Douglas Wells stepped well outside his job remit when he tried to rob a bank in 2003. When the police turned up, he revealed that he had a time bomb attached to his neck and that he was being forced to rob said bank within a certain amount of time or else the bomb would go off. The bomb turned out to be no hoax and Wells duly exploded. He wasn't just a random victim, though. It transpired that the hapless pizza delivery man was actually part of the plot to part the bank from its cash. Some plan...

Famous Last Words

'Hey, fellas! How about this for a headline for tomorrow's paper? "French Fries!"' – *James French, convicted murderer, to the press who were attending his execution by electric chair*

Celebrity Corpses

'Live fast, die young and leave a good-looking corpse' was the famous quote from the 1949 film, *Knock on Any Door*, which became synonymous with celebrities who trailed a blaze of onscreen or onstage glory, enjoyed the high life and then kicked the bucket far too early.

This chapter looks at the ugly side of stardom where the expression 'It's a wrap…' means you won't ever be coming back, and premature death can mean column inches stretching for miles as your adoring fans pore over the details of your untimely demise. There are no second takes in life, as the following collection of stories about actors, sports folk and other celebrities sadly shows.

Wrestled Into An Early Grave

In 1987, King Kong met Big Daddy in Britain and the monster ape lost. No, this wasn't a sequel to the classic movie but a showdown in the wrestling ring between Mal 'King Kong' Kirj and, ahem, Shirley 'Big Daddy' Crabtree. Around 1,500 holidaymakers had gathered to watch the two champion wrestlers fight it out, but they were horrified when 27-stone behemoth Big Daddy 'splashed' down on King Kong and his opponent suffered a fatal heart attack. While it was ruled that Big Daddy hadn't caused Kirj's death, the troubled Crabtree subsequently threw the towel in on his career. Perhaps he shouldn't have, though, because King Kong had always said, 'If I have to go, I hope it is in the ring.'

Tales Of The Macabre

Tragedy struck the wrestling world again, this time stateside, when Owen Hart, a WWF wrestler, plunged to his death in Kansas City in 1999. He was making his big entrance by being lowered from the rafters when a wire broke – he fell 70 feet, breaking his neck.

Puppy Love

The 1930s and 1940s Filipino silver screen star, Fernando Poe, died in 1951 after he contracted the dreaded disease, rabies. Initial reports stated that he had been bitten by a rabid puppy while on location filming, but it later transpired that Poe had actually cut his hand and then let the sick puppy lick the wound clean – in the process infecting the actor and condemning him to die in one of the most appalling ways imaginable.

Automatic Ending

In 1971, Terry Kath, the original guitarist and founding member of the supergroup Chicago, discovered that playing with guns is never a good idea. He picked up a 9mm automatic pistol and put it to his head in front of his wife and one of his friends. While he knew the gun's magazine was empty, Kath had forgotten that automatics can also have a bullet stored in the actual chamber of the gun. Cue: a life-ending bullet to the noggin...

Famous Last Words
'Don't worry, it's not loaded.' – *Terry Kath's last words before pulling the trigger*

When The Rhoads Ran Out...

Guitar legend Randy Rhoads was electrifying when on stage with singer Ozzy Osbourne. And like true rockers of old, he could perform offstage as well – the more hell-raising the stunt, the better. So when Rhoads decided to hitch a ride in a small plane while the band was staying in Florida, the idea of buzzing the tour bus that Ozzy was on must have seemed like a good one – even though Rhoads confessed to a fear of flying. On its fourth attempt to buzz the stationary vehicle, though, one of the plane's wings smashed into the back of the bus at an estimated speed of 140–180 mph. The plane then sliced through a pine tree before exploding, killing everyone on board.

'At approximately 9 am on Friday, March 19, 1982, I was awoken from my sleep by a loud explosion. I immediately thought that we'd hit a vehicle on the road. I got out of bed, screaming to my fiancée, Sharon, "Get off the bus!"' – *Ozzy Osbourne in a sworn affidavit about the plane incident*

Death Always Has The Last Scarf

It's a classic image of the early 20th-century starlet – slipping into a convertible car, hair blowing in the wind, a scarf flapping elegantly round her neck. It was a part that the famed dancer Isadora Duncan played to perfection in 1927, when she hitched a ride in the Bugatti of an admirer. Unfortunately for Duncan, as the car pulled away her scarf became entangled in one of the its wheels – she died instantly from a broken neck.

POP GOES CLAUDE

How many pop stars does it take to change a light bulb? Famous French crooner Claude François really should have got someone else in to change it for him. Sounds harsh, but in 1978 he had the dim idea of standing in a bath filled with water while trying to change a flickering bulb. He was electrocuted at the tender age of 39, leaving the world with that karaoke classic 'Comme d'habitude', later performed by Frank Sinatra as 'My Way'.

Ridicule Mortis
In 1923, jockey Frank Hayes won a race even though he died from a heart attack during the event – his horse, Sweet Kiss, carried on galloping and took first place.

A Leap Into Immortality

Ah, the rigours of making it in Hollywood. It can be the kind of toxic experience which makes many an actor give up and throw away their dreams – or, in the case of Peg Entwistle, throw themselves off the famous Hollywood sign. In 1932, the actress, depressed that her assault on Tinseltown had been a failure, decided on one final grand performance – so she made a poignant leap from the letter 'H' (of the sign). As if to add insult to Entwistle's fatal multiple injuries, a letter offering her a part in a play arrived two days later. It was a role to die for – her character was to commit suicide in the final act.

Silent Scream

Silent films saw the emergence of many a starlet, but one was snuffed out just as her career was igniting. In 1923, Martha Mansfield was resting in a car on the set of the period drama, *The Warrens of Virginia*, dressed in 1860s costume. Unfortunately, a member of the crew lit a cigarette and carelessly flicked the match away. It landed on Mansfield's dress and her elaborate costume burst into flames. Mansfield's co-star, Wilfred Lytell, rushed to put out the flames, but alas she died soon afterwards from an infection caused by her burns.

AiRLESS AiRPLaNE

Top US golfer Payne Stewart was being flown by Learjet to Dallas in 1999 and was only 24 minutes into the trip when air traffic control lost all contact with the pilot. An F-16 fighter plane was dispatched to track the plane and it became horribly clear that something awful had happened – the fighter pilot could see that the windows of the Learjet were iced up on the inside; the only

possible explanation was that the plane had suffered a sudden drop in cabin pressure, knocking out everyone on board before they died from lack of oxygen. The plane itself was fine – it flew on for four hours and across six states before crashing in South Dakota.

Up In Smoke

It's not how country rock pioneer Gram Parsons died in 1973 which was weird – after all, it was your common-or-garden-drug-overdose-at-a-young-age scenario – but what was freaky was what happened to his body afterwards. It was stolen from an airport by his manager and one of his friends who proceeded to drive the corpse in a hearse to the Joshua Tree National Park. There, the two doused Parsons' coffin in petrol and then lit it, creating a massive fireball. Apparently, Parsons had asked that he be cremated at the national park in the event of his death. Wish fulfilled.

Just An Act...

...Is what members of the audience were left thinking when British comedy legend, the fez-wearing Tommy Cooper, stopped halfway through his performance on stage clutching at his chest, before keeling over during a live TV broadcast. Laughter broke out as audience members took it as part of his off-the-wall act. Sadly, as they recognized that he was struggling for breath, it dawned on them that one of Britain's true comedy geniuses had just given his last performance. Cue, unscheduled commercial break...

Famous Last Words
'Either that wallpaper goes, or I do.'
– Oscar Wilde

Family Curse

Martial arts movie legend Bruce Lee's death at the age of 32 from 'a swelling of the brain' was believed to have been caused by an allergic reaction to a pharmaceutical drug, but his son Brandon Lee's death on the set of *The Crow*, the 1994 supernatural thriller, was even more outlandish. During the filming, Lee's character walked into a room and was shot. The take went fine with Lee falling to the ground as required, but once 'cut' was called, Lee didn't get back up. It transpired that a loose bullet tip had somehow found its way into the gun and this had shot out of the barrel into Lee when a harmless blank had been set off. The 28-year-old later died in hospital from internal bleeding.

Historic Remains

It's a basic human desire to leave our mark on the world; to leave a legacy that will stand the test of time, something to be remembered by. In this  chapter, many of the people featured can be seen as pioneers or great minds of their time – whether lawmakers, philosophers, the aristocracy or brand-makers – and they would all have been enshrined in the history books for their outstanding contributions alone. Alas, fate dealt them a cruel hand and made sure that, while their body of work will be remembered by historians, how they met their end is what sticks in the minds of the rest of us.

Over the following pages then, we look at the great and the good (and some of the bad) whose deaths are a significant blot on what would otherwise have been very impressive obituaries.

TEE TOETAL RECALL?

Losing one's temper and taking it out on an inanimate object is nothing new, but for Jasper Newton 'Jack' Daniel, the creator of Jack Daniel's whiskey, such an outburst proved fatal. Arriving at his office in 1911 – Jack must have had a thick head from the night before – he found he couldn't remember the combination to his safe and proceeded to kick it. Far too hard as it happens since this led to

one of his toes becoming septic and Jack dying of blood poisoning not long after. The moral of this story? When taking on a safe, it's essential to lead with the right combination.

A Tragic End

The renowned Greek playwright Aeschylus fell foul of the Grim Reaper at the claws of an eagle. The father of tragedy was killed by the bird dropping a tortoise it had clasped in its talons on to the playwright's bald head; the eagle had mistaken his bare dome for a stone. (Greek eagles use stones like we use can-openers, dropping tortoises on them from a great height to split them open so they can eat their fill.)

Death By Snacking

Stuffing one's face was a privilege that one could ill afford back in the 1700s unless one was of noble birth. Sadly, King Adolf Frederick of Sweden took this privilege rather too far during what turned out to be his final meal in 1771. He began dinner with lobster and sauerkraut, before moving on to smoked herring and caviar, all washed down with cabbage soup and champagne. For dessert, he proceeded to wolf down 14 helpings of Hetvägg, a bun stuffed with marzipan and milk. Unfortunately, the 61-year-old's digestive system was unable to cope with such an avalanche of food and he died shortly afterwards. He is now known to the Swedes as the king who 'ate himself to death'. A legacy to be proud of, then…

Going for Gold

You should always be careful what you wish for. Marcus Licinius Crassus was a Roman general who desired untold riches and would go to extraordinary lengths in pursuit of loot. His reputation obviously preceded him, for when Crassus was captured after losing a battle to the feared Parthians, they came up with a suitable punishment for the greedy blighter – he was executed by having molten gold poured down his throat.

Hu knows

Man has always gone to extraordinary lengths to conquer new frontiers and move civilization forward. For example, in AD1500, a Chinese official, Wan Hu, was fixated with the night sky and concocted a plan to be the first to travel to the stars. Hu thought the best way to achieve such a lofty goal was to tie 47 rockets to the underside of a chair and then strap himself in. He then instructed 47 of his obedient servants to light the rockets' fuses simultaneously. His menials did as they were told and moments later there was a huge explosion that blew the wannabe space pioneer to pieces.

Ridicule Mortis

The great philosopher and party animal, Chrysippus, died laughing in 207BC at the sight of his drunken donkey eating figs – while the great man's work has stood the test of time, his sense of humour has not.

Achilles' Heel, Attila's Nose

Attila the Hun was a name that struck fear into the hearts of his enemies – mainly the poor Roman empire which regularly suffered defeat at the hands of the fearsome commander and his army. But it was not to be a glorious defeat in battle that would finally see off the strapping Hun; no, it would be his wedding night and his propensity for nosebleeds. Drunk, he retired to his quarters with his new wife (the latest addition to his harem). As he staggered along to the bedchamber, the merry Attila walked into a wooden beam, smacked his nose against it and fell to the floor unconscious. He choked to death on the resultant nosebleed.

Molasses Massacre

a bizarre industrial accident in Boston in 1919 saw a tank containing 2.3 million gallons of syrup-like molasses explode, sending its contents down Boston's streets like a tsunami. The wave of molasses reached a height of 30 feet and travelled at a speed of over 30 mph, sweeping through pedestrians who were helpless to do anything: 150 people were injured and 21 folk died, choking on the liquid, unable to escape its sticky clutches…

Leap of Faith

Empedocles, the ancient Greek philosopher, hit on the idea that throwing himself into the volcano, Mount Etna, would show his disciples that he was no mere human but in fact an immortal god. Sadly, since throwing himself into the volcano in 430BC, there have been no official sightings of Empedocles the deity…

Famous Last Words
'Eat, for it is well done.' – *the last defiant words of St Lawrence as he was 'grilled' alive by the Romans on a man-sized gridiron*

Hat Splat

The term 'Draconian laws' comes from the strict laws in the 7th century BC that the Greek politician Draco codified, and which came to be seen as cruel, repressive and unnecessary, with minor crimes sometimes leading to execution. Despite his iron fist, Draco proved to be very popular with the citizens of Athens – so popular in fact that they inadvertently killed him in a fit of adulation. After he had finished a speech, the crowd threw their hats, shirts and tunics into the air to celebrate his wise words: this huge mass of clothing then landed on Draco and suffocated him.

Boweled Over

A controversial figure of his time, the priest Arius was branded a heretic by the Christian Church for his challenging views on religion and the nature of Jesus Christ. But for many, it was the graphic and bizarre nature of his death in AD336 that lingers morbidly in the mind. Perhaps the words written by the Church historian Socrates Scholasticus best sum up what happened on that fart-ful day when Arius experienced 'a violent relaxation of the bowels… Soon after, a faintness came over him, and together with the evacuations his bowels protruded, followed by a copious haemorrhage, and the descent of the smaller intestines: moreover portions of his spleen and liver were brought off in the effusion of blood, so that he almost immediately died.'

Ridicule Mortis

The great Renaissance philosopher and scientist of the 1600s, Sir Francis Bacon, met his maker when a spur-of-the-moment experiment went wrong – he wondered if snow could preserve flesh so he decided to find out by killing a chicken and replacing its insides with the white stuff. Because of the chill he caught, though, Bacon died in bed just days later.

Ridicule Mortis
Renowned for his epic
beard – believed to be a
whopping six feet long –
Austrian Hans Steininger
tripped on it and died while
racing away from a fire
in 1567.

Bad Bladder

The famous 16th-century Danish astronomer, Tycho Brahe, was often invited to high-society banquets. The one he attended on 13 October 1601, though, was to be his last. After consuming copious amounts of wine, he realized that a trip to the toilet was essential. Alas, as a stickler for etiquette, the astronomer did not wish to offend his host by leaving for the 'comfort station' halfway through a meal. So he held and held and held until the interminable feast was over. Sadly, when Tycho went to relieve himself, he found himself unable to wee properly – his self-imposed hiatus had induced an infection, which ravaged him mercilessly for 12 days. He suffered fever, dizziness and bouts of unconsciousness before he passed away.

Nightcapped

Known for his love of fine living and consumption (as well as the odd venereal disease or two), the 17th-century poet Thomas May was somewhat overweight. It is said that when he retired to bed he would tie his nightcap tightly under his many

chins before drifting off to sleep. On one occasion, though, he did not wake up – the cord was so tight that when he rolled over it pulled ever tighter and choked him to death.

Udderly Terrible

Nancy Hanks Lincoln gave the world Abraham Lincoln, but in return fate dealt her a cruel hand in 1818, courtesy of a cow. After drinking some milk, Nancy fell victim to 'milk sickness', which occurs when a victim ingests milk from a cow that has eaten the toxic white snakeroot plant. The plant's poison makes its way into the cow's milk and then inevitably into the human food chain. It took just under two agonizing weeks for the mother of one of America's most important presidents to die.

Ridicule Mortis
The esteemed Scottish writer and translator, Sir Thomas Urquhart, died in 1660 after bursting into hysterical laughter on hearing that Charles II had been reinstated as king.

32

You Can't Take It With You...

The all-conquering wrestler, Yousouf Ishmaelo, known as 'The Terrible Turk', was on his way back from America in 1898 when his liner hit another vessel and began to sink. While the Turk was certainly strong enough to save his own life, Ishmaelo refused to take off the money belt that contained the winnings from his crushingly successful tour of the US. Thus 'The Terrible Turk' drowned, taking his many gold coins with him to the ocean floor.

Big Mouth

If you're given a pardon by the Tsar of Russia, then it's best you bow modestly, turn round slowly and high-tail it off the premises. Unlike Russian poet and revolutionary Kondraty Fyodorovich Ryleyev – in 1826, his mouth earned him a death sentence. Fortunately, the rope he was being hanged with snapped and, as was tradition at the time, a botched execution meant a pardon would be issued. Alas, as the

Tsar was reluctantly about to sign Ryleyev's reprieve, he heard the gobby revolutionary declaring: 'You see, in Russia they don't know how to do anything; they can't even make rope.' Ryleyev was promptly sent back to the gallows for another attempt. This time, the rope held.

Isn't It Ironic?

Over millennia, evolution may have spruced up the human race a bit and science may have made life a lot more comfortable, but you can still never be complacent or drop your guard for even the shortest time. Indeed, the following stories demonstrate that you should also never laugh in the face of Death, but instead you should apologize to him profusely before disappearing over the horizon super smart quick – preferably without tripping over the shoelaces of your most prized trainers and accidentally killing yourself.

In other words, don't take life for granted or else those that control our fates may decide you don't deserve it – as the following people sadly discovered far too late.

Reality Check Please

I f you managed to survive a 10,000-volt electrical shock, you might think you were lucky; that by sheer fluke, you managed to slip through the Grim Reaper's fingers and lived to fight (or fry) another day. Alas for Russian 42-year-old Dmitry Butakov, such a shocking experience only made him think that he was immortal. So deeply convinced was Butakov that he invited the press to witness him defy death once again, this time by drinking antifreeze. After starting on his second bottle, Butakov experienced a severe and extreme reality check when mortality politely tapped him on the shoulder and he slipped into a coma. The next day, he passed away.

Famous Last Words

'It won't be a problem. I'll be strapped to my instructor.' – *54-year-old Mexican woman to her friend before she made a parachute jump with her instructor to overcome her fear of heights. The main parachute failed and, 8,500 feet later, they were killed on impact.*

Jim'll Fixx It

I f you find yourself jogging and wonder which idiot managed to turn such a miserable pastime into a global phenomenon, then you can thank Jim Fixx. When his book, *The Complete Book of Running*, was published in 1978, its message was that jogging was a vital part of keeping one's heart in good shape; a jogging craze subsequently swept America and inevitably the rest of the western world. In 1984, though, this guru of physical fitness was jogging in Vermont when he collapsed and died of a heart attack at the age of 52. An autopsy revealed that the arteries of Fixx's heart were in terrible condition – his left coronary artery was nearly completely blocked while only 20 per cent of his right artery was clear…

Famous Last Words

'I've decided to live to be a hundred. I never felt better in my life!' – *72-year-old Jerome Irving Rodale, publisher of* Organic Farming & Gardening *magazine, interviewed for an unaired episode of* The Dick Cavett Show *in 1971. Moments after his interview, he died of a heart attack on set.*

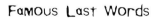

World's Most Dead-icated Lawyer

FaMOus Last Words
'My God, I've shot myself!' – lawyer Clement L Vallandigham on discovering that the pistol he'd fired had been loaded

If you had been alive in the 1800s and had found yourself in a spot of bother in Ohio, Clement L Vallandigham would have been the man to turn to before his untimely death in 1871. Ohio politician-turned-lawyer Vallandigham was representing Thomas McGehan on charges of murder after it was alleged he had shot and killed Tom Myers in a bar. Being of sharp mind, Vallindigham was convinced that Myers had in fact shot himself by accident while pulling out his gun. The lawyer was convinced he could prove it, so on the evening before the trial he showed his defence team how it must have happened. He pulled out a pistol and then, enacting what he believed Myers must have done, fired it. Vallandigham hadn't realized that the gun was loaded and he died from his injury soon after. His legacy? Thomas McGehan was freed. Job done.

Dead Wrong

Hit TV crime series *CSI* has become an unstoppable money-making global franchise thanks to its gross-out depictions of the forensics used to solve fictional murders and tragedies; but it has inadvertently caused real-life tragedy too. 55-year-old Earl F Ellwanger of South Dakota was adamant that a scene in *CSI* was inaccurate; the scene featured the TV crime team's view that it was impossible that a female victim could have shot herself in the stomach. To prove his point, Ellwanger used a shotgun to illustrate how it was in fact very possible, sadly not twigging that his gun was loaded. Unfortunately, he died from his self-inflicted injuries two days later – at least Ellwanger can rest easy in the knowledge that he proved *CSI* wrong. Dead wrong.

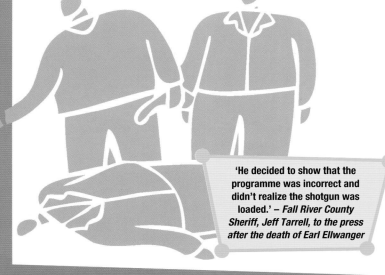

'He decided to show that the programme was incorrect and didn't realize the shotgun was loaded.' – *Fall River County Sheriff, Jeff Tarrell, to the press after the death of Earl Ellwanger*

The Fast and the Feckless

Fast cars and young men don't mix – especially when you flip the finger in the face of Death. Take Austrian Helmut Mezer, who had been given a BMW for his 18th birthday. The car featured a personalized plate DEAD1 and, days later, Mr G Reaper decided that enough was enough. Mezer died in his car after crashing at 100 mph.

Famous Last Words

'They couldn't hit an elephant at this distance.' – *General John Sedgwick at the battle of Spotsylvania in 1862 seconds before being killed by an enemy bullet*

Anger Mismanagement

You should always practise what you preach; something anger-management counsellor, Charles Mahuka, probably wished he'd borne in mind. One of his 'students', Miguel Gonzalez, turned up drunk to a session and began causing mayhem. Mahuka lost his temper and hurled himself at his client, attacking him so violently that Gonzalez ended up in a coma that he never came out of.

No Cheating!

Convicted of first degree murder, 40-year-old Robert Brecheen was set to be executed in 1995, but decided to cheat the authorities by taking an overdose of sedatives. However, his plan was discovered by prison guards and his life was saved by a stomach pump at the local hospital. Brecheen was then taken back to the prison and promptly executed by lethal injection. The overdose only delayed the inevitable by two hours.

Famous Last Words
'Go away... I'm all right.' – *visionary author, H G Wells*

Famous Last Words

'No, you certainly can't.' – *what John F Kennedy is believed to have said to the wife of Dallas' governor after she told him,* 'You certainly can't say that the people of Dallas haven't given you a nice welcome, Mr President.'

Inventor Interruptus

Many scientists start off with the best of intentions but some can inadvertently end up causing immeasurable harm. Take Thomas Midgley who has been heralded as the person who has done the most damage to the environment thanks to his inventions of ozone-destroying CFCs and leaded petrol in the first half of the 20th century. Fortunately, his highly creative side managed to stop him from doing any more harm by inadvertently bringing his activities to a halt with another well-meaning but dangerous invention. Because of a medical condition, Midgley had a severe physical disability so he built a contraption to lift himself in and out of bed. Sadly, Midgley became entangled in the ropes used in the device and he suffocated.

41

Just Desserts

Some folk are just asking for it. Call it divine retribution, reaping what you sow or just being a bloody idiot, sometimes Fate responds by giving you exactly what you asked for, whether you like it or not.

So let the following stories remind you to think very carefully about how you go about getting what you want – or else you could end up as a cadaver on the mean streets of life being laughed at by passers-by. It's a harsh lesson for sure, but mankind has had a lot of those. How else do you think we learned to survive on this planet?

FUNERAL SERVICE

Keep On Truckin'

We should start this entry with a clear warning – do not try this at home, or on any road in your neighbourhood. It may seem like obvious advice, but 18-year-old Michael A Shingledecker must have wished he had remembered it when he decided to lie down in the middle of a Pennsylvanian road in 1993, inspired by a dare portrayed in the movie *The Program*. He was duly run over by a pick-up truck and killed. Meanwhile, in New Jersey three days later, drunken 24-year-old handyman, Marco Birkhimer, decided that replicating the movie's stunt would be a great idea for him too – and he was struck dead by two cars.

THE MOLE STRIKES BACK

Some people go to extraordinary lengths to rid themselves of the humble garden mole, but an unnamed German man in his sixties went all the way. Herr Brained, as we shall call him, drove a series of metal rods deep into his lawn. He then connected them to a high-voltage power line in the hope of frying the moles in their holes. In fact, he did a remarkably effective job of electrifying the entire garden, including the patch of turf on which he was standing. Sadly, it was a case of Herr Today, Gone Tomorrow…

Cact-die!

You don't want to cross Mother Nature – especially while wielding a loaded shotgun and, presumably, sporting an IQ of less than 50. David Grundman learnt this lesson in the harshest way imaginable in 1982 when he headed out into the desert armed with a shotgun for a spot of 'cactus plugging'. This 'sport' involves finding a cactus and then shooting it repeatedly in an effort to make yourself feel heroic. Grundman blasted a four-foot arm off a towering 100-year-old cactus, which promptly toppled on top of him, sending him remarkably swiftly up the stairway to heaven. Crushing stuff indeed.

Ridicule Mortis

1985: Over 100 lifeguards throw a pool party in New Orleans; four of them oversee the event. They only notice a drowned party-goer at the end of the bash. Retraining all round, we think…

A Word Of Warning

When you light a cigarette in the comfort of your own home and it sends blue flames shooting up to the ceiling, it's best to call the authorities. If said authorities then tell you not to light another cigarette before they have come round to inspect the property, it's probably a good idea to listen to them. The Pawliks family must have thought otherwise, though – they didn't follow the advice they were given and subsequently two members of the family were killed by violent explosions that ripped through their house. These were caused by an odourless gas leak from a broken main, which was then ignited by the mother of the family who decided on a quick smoke before the inspector came round. The surviving members of the family sued the gas company and, incredibly, actually reached an undisclosed settlement. Only in America…

Flaming Idiot!

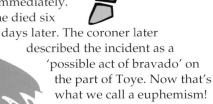

43-year-old Michael Toye showed real spirit when he declared to his friend one drink-fuelled evening that white spirit – a form of paraffin – was not in fact flammable. To prove his point, Toye poured the highly flammable liquid over himself before lighting it. The resulting fireball consumed his arms, thighs and chest. The flames were put out by his friend who then told Toye that he should go to hospital immediately. Sadly, Toye refused and he died six days later. The coroner later described the incident as a 'possible act of bravado' on the part of Toye. Now that's what we call a euphemism!

'I'm all right. I just want a fag and a beer.' –*Michael Toye to his friend who had just put him out*

Oh Mein Gotz!

W ell, you have to admire German Adam Gotz's faith. Here was a young man who believed that he was a 'spiritual psychiatrist' and, while visiting the pyramids in Egypt, told his girlfriend that the spiritual energy given off by the ancient structures would help him 'transcend humanity' and be 'free from death'. A member of an obscure cult that worships the Egyptian god-kings, he told her nothing could stop him from being resurrected. To prove his point, he climbed to the top of the tallest building in Egypt, the Cairo Tower, and to everyone's horror proceeded to jump from it. He died after a 600-foot fall and his girlfriend is still waiting to hear from him. Gotz jumped back in 1998.

Ridicule Mortis

Two men drowned after stealing a kayak and heading out on to Moon Lake in Florida. The boat capsized and it became clear to observers that neither of them knew how to swim, or had bothered with a life jacket. Glug, glug, glug…

47

The Fall Guy

The mean streets of San Francisco are patrolled by ever-vigilant police on the lookout for car thieves. Sadly, some of the car thieves themselves don't have the cops' observational skills. One car thief was spotted by police exiting a car he had broken into and they yelled at him to stop. No chance – the thief took off like a gazelle, fleeing from his pursuers. Seeing a low wall up ahead, he made for it, jumping over the three-foot obstacle. It was at this moment he must have realized his fatal error – because on the other side of the wall was a 200-foot drop. He fell and died at the scene.

Ridicule Mortis

Veteran skydiving instructor Ivan McGuire must have been starstruck when he decided to film himself making a 3,000m jump in North Carolina in 1988. While he remembered the camera, wearing an actual parachute completely slipped his mind... it was his last jump.

The RIP Factor

There can be a harsh penalty to pay if you sing out of tune in the Philippines, as was the case when 29-year-old Romy Baligula took to the stage in his local karaoke bar in San Mateo and began belting out his rendition of Frank Sinatra's 'My Way'. It didn't go down well and a security guard shouted out that Baligula was out of tune. Undeterred, Baligula persevered. It proved to be a fatal mistake – his punishment for continuing to murder Frank Sinatra's classic was to be murdered himself by said guard who pulled out his gun and shot Baligula dead.

Because the song has been known to lead to fights that have resulted in several fatalities, Sinatra's song is banned by many karaoke bars in the Philippines.

Just Train Stupid

A 68-year-old woman in Anaheim, California, can't have been thinking too clearly when she found her Honda Civic stuck on a level crossing with a freight train bearing down on her. Instead of getting out of the car and running, she decided to call the police instead and ask them what to do. She died at the scene.

Love Lost...
Drawn &
Quartered

Love drives us crazy and can make us do ridiculous things to win over the objects of our affections. We can write sonnets; serenade our heart's desire with a song; send flowers and gifts; or impale ourselves on the handlebars of motorbikes while trying to flee our rage-filled partners. In fact, judging by the following catalogue of loved-up lunacy, perhaps we should all remain single.

While some would say that it is better to have loved and lost than never to have loved at all, what they don't realize is that it is in fact often safer never to have loved at all than to have lost your life. And don't go thinking that the platonic love you feel for your friends and family is any safer either...

It's In Her Kiss

'**D**on't make promises you can't keep' is the moral of this tawdry tale of infidelity. Sweethearts since childhood, Xin Xinfeng and her beau, Mao Ansheng, from Yunnan province, made a pact that if one of them ever cheated on the other, they would pay for the indiscretion with their life. It was an oath that Xinfeng took very seriously… far too seriously perhaps. She spotted Ansheng flirting with another woman and subsequently arranged to meet her man in a public bathhouse the following day. One snog later and he was dead – she had put rat poison in a plastic pellet, placed said pellet under her tongue and then pushed it into her lover's mouth as they kissed. For her crime of passion, Xinfeng was sentenced to death. As Confucius once wrote, 'When you embark on a journey of revenge, better to start by digging two graves.'

Poisonous Popularity

The Chinese love their poisons. For disgruntled couples it seems the weapon of choice: a couple having an affair spiked their respective partners' food. And thanks to bitter family feuds, even funerals can become toxic: 34 people fell ill at one after ingesting food laced with a toxic poison and, at another, the widow laced the food with rat poison, killing ten of the guests.

Cheers Up, Heads Down

Best to keep your head down when receiving good news as François Faber found out in 1915. He was overjoyed when he was told he was now the proud father of a daughter. So happy was Faber that he cheered loudly and leapt up out of the First World War trench he was ensconced in. He was immediately shot and killed by an enemy sniper.

COFFIN Catastrophe

It was already a traumatic day for the Brazilian Silveria Coimbra family as they headed to the cemetery to bury their father. But it was rendered twice as bad when the hearse they were travelling in was hit from behind. The coffin shot forward, hitting the wife of the deceased and killing her on the spot.

Cable Guy

In 1998, 25-year-old Juan Taphanel became enraged at losing an argument he was having with his wife – so he pushed her out of the window. She would have plummeted eight floors if her fall hadn't been broken by cables. Perhaps regretting his unchivalrous behaviour, Taphanel attempted to rescue her but ended up falling to his own death. His wife survived. Remember, women are always right – learn that and you will live longer.

Let's Get Physical

Being exercised to death by your transsexual wife sounds like a death made up by a bad fiction writer, but for 73-year-old James Mason it became a tragic fact. In June 2008, 41-year-old Christine Newton-John (previously known as John Vallandingham) was filmed on CCTV pulling her husband, Mason, round a swimming pool by his legs and arms, only stopping to push his head under the water. On 43 separate occasions, she stopped Mason from getting out of the pool and watched dispassionately as he desperately tried to catch his breath while clinging to the pool's side. The video showed that the session lasted one hour and 40 minutes and, when it was over, Mason suffered a fatal heart attack. Newton-John pleaded guilty to reckless homicide.

'Mr. Mason was very afraid of water. So afraid of water he'd seldom bathe. He did not exercise and had health problems.' – *Police Chief Joseph A Stehlik on the weird death of James Mason at the hands of his wife*

Queen Of Corpses

Death can be weird but how you treat the corpse afterwards can be so much stranger – or just plain insane if you were King Pedro of Portugal. For his coronation in 1361, he insisted that the love of his life, Inêz de Castro, be present so she could be crowned queen. The problem was that she was dead, murdered by knights – an event that many believe had driven Pedro mad. He had her dug up and, at the wedding, nobles had to bow before Inêz's corpse and kiss her rotting hand. Then King Pedro had two of her murderers executed as part of the coronation celebrations – they were tortured in front of the guests before having their hearts ripped out.

Impress and Pass Out

Chivalry is not dead – it's just the chivalrous men who gave up their lives to help a damsel in distress that are. In this case, said damsel was a student in Kenya who managed to drop her phone down a latrine she was using. After she had offered money to anyone brave enough to venture down the dank, stinking and putrid hole, three men dared the descent, one after another, never to return after encountering noxious fumes. The phone never turned up.

Going Public

Arguments between loved ones can flare up in the most unexpected places; even in the middle of a busy road. While travelling along the Trans-Canada Highway at night in a taxi, a squabbling couple demanded that the cab pull over. The woman then got out, her partner following her. Drivers were horrified to see the couple, lit by headlights, continuing the fight in the middle of the road. Several strikes by cars later, the couple's argument came to an abrupt end with both partners lying silent on the road.

'We thought we'd hit a cow or a piece of lumber, but we'd apparently run over two individuals that had already been hit. We weren't the first ones; I think we were car No. 4.' – *shaken driver to reporters after the fatal incident*

Train Wreck

It's like a scene from a movie. Take one man who's had enough of his life and his relationship. Place him in a car with his unsuspecting girlfriend and then watch in bemusement as he parks his car on a railroad. Then flinch in horror as a train thunders towards them and smashes into the side of said car. Then breathe a sigh of relief that the girlfriend survived the smash, despite the fact that the boyfriend was thrown from the car and killed. That old adage, 'You're better off without him', never rang so true.

Handlebar Hell

Sleeping with another man's wife can be a fraught and dangerous affair as Colombian Emilio Garcia found out when he fled on hearing his lover's husband arrive home. One jump from the second floor window of his lover's apartment later and Emilio must have seen his life flash before his eyes as his crotch embedded itself in the handlebars of his motorbike which he had parked below. He later died from his injuries. What was so wrong with hiding in the cupboard like everyone else?

What Price Love?

S ome people will go to extraordinary lengths to try and win back a former lover. Take Kathleen Yeoman, a 46-year-old single mum in Northamptonshire, who thought the best way to win back neighbour Paul Cockerhill's heart was to pretend her house had been burgled. The plan saw Kathleen trash her house and then tape her own mouth shut, before placing a plastic bag over her head and tying her own hands together. She then lay down on Cockerhill's doorstep

and waited for him to come home. Alas, while lying there, Yeoman threw up – but because of her tied hands, she was unable to remove the tape from her mouth. By the time Cockerhill did make it home, Yeoman had expired after choking on her own vomit. The police only figured out the full circumstances of her death when they realized nothing had actually been taken during the supposed burglary and she had £918 in her handbag.

Cack-Hand-Ed

A complicated love triangle resulted in a complicated death in 1994 when Florida resident, Edward Hand, discovered that his lover, Kathy Gauley, was about to return to her estranged husband, Ronald. A bizarre showdown between the three resulted in Hand pulling out a gun and trying to commit suicide in front of the couple by placing the gun under his chin and pulling the trigger. The bullet made it as far as Hand's mouth before ricocheting off his teeth and ripping out of his right cheek. The lethal missile's final destination was Ronald Gauley's head. He was killed on the spot.

Mad Axe

a word of warning – falling foul of a good tickling can land you with a murder charge. Vietnamese 65-year-old Siek Phan was chopping firewood with an axe when her beloved husband, Nou Meas, launched a surprise tickling attack from behind. Shocked at this, Phan swung the axe round behind her. A split second later, she turned to see her husband lying motionless on the ground, his head almost removed from his shoulders. The widow was subsequently charged with murder.

Hair Loss

Blood may be thicker than water, but it doesn't stand a chance against wounded vanity. Frenchman Thierry Sigaud was so incensed by a haircut his mother gave him that he shot and killed the poor woman. When his father rushed to her aid, Sigaud then turned the gun on him.

Losing his Head

Some spouses don't know when to let go – clinging on long after a relationship hits the rocks. In 1993, American GI Gregory Glover's body was found in a phone box at a German airfield – but his head was nowhere to be seen. No, furious husband and fellow GI Stephen Schap had removed that and taken it with him after discovering that Glover had got his wife up the duff. Meanwhile, Mrs Schap was in hospital recovering from complications to do with her pregnancy when Schap marched into her hospital room with a bag, opened it and then pulled out Glover's head. Doctors found Diane screaming and the head placed on the nightstand next to her bed.

'Look, Diane – Glover's here! He'll sleep with you every night now. Only you won't sleep – because all you'll see is this.' – *Diane Schap's estranged husband to her as he revealed the decapitated head of her lover, Gregory Glover*

Silly Stiffs

It may seem harsh, distasteful and even offensive to label someone's death as 'silly', but the manner of the following deaths makes any other adjective redundant. So use these stories to remind yourself that the worst imaginable deaths can be brought about by your very own hand – with a little help from copious amounts of alcohol, water, shopping trolleys, Nintendo Wiis and more.

You could be forgiven for thinking that the Grim Reaper lurks around every corner, just waiting for you to slip up while laughing as he brings his scythe down on you – or in the case of the chap on page 69, an axe wielded by a friend.

BOOTLEG BOOZE

60

Uh-Oh, Urine Trouble!

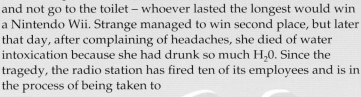

It's not unknown for people to go to extreme lengths to win a competition, but Californian mother of three, Jennifer Strange, ended up paying with her life in 2007. She was taking part in a radio competition entitled 'Hold your Wee for a Wii' where contestants were asked to drink copious amounts of water and not go to the toilet – whoever lasted the longest would win a Nintendo Wii. Strange managed to win second place, but later that day, after complaining of headaches, she died of water intoxication because she had drunk so much H_2O. Since the tragedy, the radio station has fired ten of its employees and is in the process of being taken to court.

Ridicule Mortis

Robert Williams, a worker at the Ford factory in Michigan, was one of the first people to be killed by a robot. In 1979, he was struck on the head by the arm of a robot 'designed to retrieve parts from storage' and died instantly.

Berserk for Berzerk

There's no harm in playing the odd videogame but there are several examples of people taking their love of gaming to excess and paying the ultimate price. What is believed to be the first death 'caused' by a videogame was that of 19-year-old Jeff Dailey in 1981, who finished amassing a massive score in *Berzerk* before collapsing and dying from a heart attack. A year later, an 18-year-old, Peter Burkowski, died in similar circumstances after playing the same game.

Should Have Grabbed Fifty Winks

The South Korean 28-year-old, Lee Seung Seop, had already quit his job so he could dedicate more time to playing videogames – it's a highly competitive and very lucrative sport in Korea. But in 2005, Lee lost everything when he collapsed and died after playing the popular title, *Starcraft*, for 50 hours almost non-stop. It is believed that he died from heart failure caused by exhaustion. But he wasn't the first Korean to push himself beyond the limit. In 2002, a 22-year-old was found dead in the toilet of an Internet cafe after spending a staggering 86 hours honing his videogame skills…

Game For A Laugh

The hit UK comedy show of the 70s, *The Goodies*, not only caused outbreaks of hysterical laughter up and down Britain, but it also caused a death in 1975. 50-year-old bricklayer Alex Mitchell suffered heart failure when he broke into a 25-minute fit of laughter after watching the *Goodies* sketch, 'Kung Fu Kapers'. His wife took the death graciously – she actually wrote to the *Goodies* to thank them for ensuring that her husband's last moments were happy ones.

A Sheep Hit

Pity poor Betty Stobbs in 1999 who was besieged by her flock of sheep as she fed them hay from the back of her quad bike. So ravenous were the sheep that they inadvertently pushed her off a cliff and down into a quarry in Stanhope. She is believed to have survived the fall, but the quad bike landing on her seconds later finished her off.

Ridicule Mortis

Over 2,500 left-handers are killed each year using devices that are designed for right-handers. Be particularly wary of the right-handed power saw, the number one killer of left-handed people.

The Hoarders' Comeuppance

Two brothers, Homer and Langley Collyer, lived together in Manhattan. They had become recluses, known for never throwing anything away. In 1947, the police, acting on a tip-off that someone had

died in the house, cut their way into the property to discover a mass of junk and booby traps amid a bewildering network of passages and tunnels. After crawling round the house for two hours they managed to find a body – that of the blind brother, Homer. Days later, they also found Langley's dead, rat-gnawed body, ten feet from his sibling; he had fallen foul of one of the brothers' own booby traps, leaving his blind brother to fend unsuccessfully for himself. The time it took to locate Langley's body might sound like incompetence on the police's part, but by the time the house was cleared, the authorities had removed 25,000 books, 14 pianos, 103 tons of rubbish and hundreds of thousands of old newspapers.

A Real Pane

With the blessed gift of hindsight, perhaps 39-year-old Toronto lawyer, Garry Hoy, might have thought never to put one's faith in inanimate objects. One Friday evening in 1993, he was showing law students just how robust the windows of the law firm's skyscraper were. To prove his point – apparently one he had made before – he barged the window with his shoulder. Unfortunately on this occasion, the window decided not to play ball and popped out of its frame. Hoy fell 24 floors to his death.

LiFE Imitating Art

After hours of drinking, 31-year-old Emma Blackwell was believed to have plunged to her death on a ferry off the coast of France after trying to emulate Kate Winslet's outstretched-arm pose from the film, *Titanic*. Unlike the Oscar-winning actress, Blackwell slipped and fell nine decks to her death.

'She liked to lark about.' – *Blackwell's sister after the coroner's hearing*

Join The Club

Bad sportsmanship can leave a bad taste in the mouth or, in this particular case, a golf club in the chest. Jeremy Brenno, a 16-year-old New Yorker, became so frustrated with the way he was playing that he lashed out at a bench with a No. 3 Wood. The club's shaft broke and rebounded, puncturing his chest and piercing his heart.

Ridicule Mortis

150 people a year are killed by falling coconuts. Sounds unlikely but bear in mind that they can reach speeds of 50 mph falling from 80 feet.

Bowl Bereavement

Found drowned in your cat's water bowl may sound impossible but it became a ridiculous reality for New Zealander Peter John Robinson. Suffering from balance problems because he was born with only one ear, Robinson slipped on some ice as he walked over to feed his cat, Piper. He fell, smacked his head and landed with his face in the cat's water bowl. Robinson proceeded to drown in three and a half inches of water.

Thirst For Death

A 19-year-old Ontario student, Kevin Mackle, decided that he was feeling particularly parched at four in the morning, so he headed to the nearest drinks machine. It is believed that the drunken student tried to skip paying by sticking his arm up into its innards. Due to his violent rocking of the machine, the 1,000-pound drink dispenser toppled over and crushed him to death.

Between 1978 and 1995, 37 deaths and 113 injuries were caused by vending machines in the US which toppled over on to angry, frustrated or thieving consumers.

ANT ATTACK

After inadvertently swallowing some ants, Egyptian farmhand Susu Borai Mohammad was so worried that they might bite her once they were in her stomach that she drank some insecticide to make sure they were good and dead. Shortly afterwards, she followed them to the great anthill in the sky.

The Human Fireburp

'The explosion was so catastrophic that much of Mr Cazacu's body was vapourized, making a post-mortem impossible.' – official spokesperson for the circus

Romanian fire-eater Vlad Cazacu was an old hand at the flame game, but he made a fatal mistake when he inadvertently swallowed the flammable liquid that he was holding in his mouth during a performance. Such liquid is normally spat out at the fiery torch held in the fire-eater's hand to produce an audience-wowing fireball. On this occasion though, Cazacu burped after swallowing the liquid while the torch was only inches from his face. He exploded as the flammable vapour from his belch caught light and blazed its way back down into his stomach.

Par-fect Manners

Malaysian lawyer Anthony Phua was enjoying his first time on a golf course with a friend. Relaxing before attending a wedding, he walked up behind said buddy as he took a swing. The golf club hit Phua in the neck and he was whacked unconscious but only for a moment. Showing commendable golfing etiquette, Phua came round, got up and apologized for getting in the way of his friend's stroke. And then he keeled over and died.

Bubblegum's A Bummer

Pride comes before a fall. Or in the case of Australian Abner Kriller, pride in blowing a large bubble with bubblegum while driving his car. The bubble popped, causing the gum to cover his glasses and obscure his vision. Cue: the predicted fall – down the side of a hill and to his death.

POLE AXED

Drink, men and axes don't mix as Polish farmer Krzystof Azninski should have known after spending a day in 1995 drinking with three buddies. The madcap events of the day had already seen the men strip naked and hit each other over the head with turnips, but for the climax of the party Azninski dared a friend to take an axe to his neck, believing that he would not be brave enough to do it. Unfortunately, Azninski was proven wrong.

Strange Suicides

It's an issue that is usually taboo, but it's impossible not to laugh when you hear how some people have chosen to end their lives. In fact, you know that the person who took their own life in such spectacular fashion wanted people to keep talking about their final 'statement' long after they had gone.

There can be no other explanation for the outlandish examples of the ultimate in self-destruction featured in the following pages. So think of this chapter as a ghoulish tribute to those who came up with wild, inventive and terminal ideas to leave their mark on this world; they'll be talked, and written, about for years to come.

In loving memory

Political Manoeuvring

Accused of mail fraud, racketeering and conspiracy, Pennsylvania state treasurer Budd Dwyer was found guilty on all charges in 1987 and was facing up to 55 years in prison. Dwyer, though, was adamant that he was innocent, even turning down a plea bargain. So when he called a press conference the day before his sentencing, journalists expected him to make one final declaration of innocence and resign from his post before they locked him up and threw away the key. Instead, after giving a rambling speech about being a victim of a conspiracy to destroy him, Dwyer pulled out a gun, put the barrel in his mouth and pulled the trigger, his suicide infamously being caught on TV cameras.

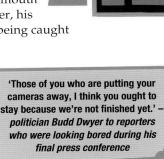

'Those of you who are putting your cameras away, I think you ought to stay because we're not finished yet.' – *politician Budd Dwyer to reporters who were looking bored during his final press conference*

Chainsaw Crusader

David Phyall, 58, had been told that the block of flats where he lived in Southampton was being pulled down and that he would have to find alternative accommodation. But even when he was offered somewhere else to live, Phyall was having none of it. Threatened with eviction, he decided to make the ultimate protest. He plugged in the power lead of an electric chainsaw and set a timer to start the chainsaw. Phyall then tied the chainsaw to a table leg and taped the power switch into the 'on' position. That done, he took a cocktail of drugs and waited, his neck resting on the blade of the chainsaw. Once the timer went into action, the chainsaw spun into life, cutting off Phyall's head.

> 'I find he did it [cut off his head] to draw attention to the injustice he felt at being asked to move out of his flat.'
> – *the verdict delivered by the Hampshire coroner*

Suicide Machine

Unhappy that his family were putting him under pressure to move into a retirement home, 81-year-old Australian Francis Tovey decided that enough was enough in 2008. So after researching a 'suicide robot' online, he constructed an elaborate contraption featuring a jigsaw power tool with a semi-automatic pistol attached to it – the intention being that the power tool would activate the gun when Tovey wanted it to. He then put this bizarre device up on his driveway. Some time later, a neighbour heard three gunshots and raced over to find Tovey dead in the driveway.

Carmageddon

It must have been a gruelling sight for motorists in South Wales as 54-year-old Gerald Mellin's open-top Aston Martin DB7 slowly drove past with his body in the driver's seat – and his head in the back. Bitter and angry after separating from his wife in 2008, Mellin decided that the best way of getting back at her was to separate his head from his body. He'd tied one end of a rope round a tree and the other around his neck before going for his final drive. Point proven, we think…

A Fateful Landing

Suicides are notorious for going wrong (or right, depending on your point of view). But some people leave nothing to chance. One well-prepared former Bournemouth hotel owner and millionaire, Terry Brand, spent three months learning to fly in 1997. The newly qualified pilot then took off in a light aircraft and radioed air traffic controllers so they could give his apologies 'to everyone'. Brand then flew into the sea. An inquest revealed that the dead man had recently become a Buddhist and believed that suicide was his destiny.

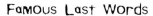

Tabloid TV

In 1974, Florida viewers were shocked when 29-year-old newscaster, Christine Chubbuck, pulled out a gun eight minutes into her news bulletin and shot herself in the head on live television. Viewers may have realized that something was amiss moments before when Chubbuck announced that 'in keeping with Channel 40's policy of bringing you the latest in blood and guts, and in living colour, you are going to see another first: an attempted suicide'. The bullet wound did not kill her immediately, but Chubbuck passed away 14 hours later.

Famous Last Words

'They tried to get me – I got them first!' *Poet Vachel Lindsay who killed himself by drinking a bottle of disinfectant in 1931. He was plagued by money worries and ill-health.*

Make Your Mind Up

An Italian woman decided that she'd had a gutful of life's slings and arrows, so she proceeded to douse herself in petrol by the River Ticino. Igniting herself with a match, she was overcome with fear, changed her mind and leapt into the river. She drowned.

THE Big ChiLL

Still reeling after separating from his wife, Australian Cory Quinn decided to have the last word on their failing marriage when she went on vacation. He bought 154 pounds of meat and then placed it and himself in their home's walk-in freezer before dying of hypothermia. When the 20-stone wife returned home from her holiday, she found a note on the door of the freezer that stated: 'Gorge on this, you fat pig!'

Going Off Big Time!

Excessive depression plus an insider's knowledge of explosives can be a lethal cocktail. Take Bohumil Sole, the 63-year-old scientist believed to be one of the boffins who dreamt up Semtex – he strapped the explosive to himself in 1997 and then went to a spa in the Czech Republic where he was being treated for depression. Sole managed to level the building when he blew himself to smithereens. Remarkably, no one else was killed.

Mad Chef

So unhappy was a renowned French chef of the 17th century, François Vatel, when a fish delivery he needed for a royal banquet was late, that he killed himself using his own sword. Sounds insane but it is claimed that the chef hadn't slept in days, so busy was he preparing for the royal visit.

Famous Last Words

'Pardon me, sir. I did not do it on purpose.' – *Marie Antoinette after she inadvertently stepped on the foot of the man who was about to execute her*

Webcam Horror

In what was believed to be one of the world's first online suicides, Brit Kevin Whitrick told an online chat room in 2007 that he was going to top himself. The chatroom was set up for people to insult each other as a way of letting off steam and was packed with over 50 users, some of whom egged Whitrick on. He switched on his webcam and then broadcast himself tying a rope to a ceiling joist. Climbing on to a chair, he then slipped the noose round his neck while some members of the chatroom goaded him on, with one member saying, 'F***ing do it!' over and over again. Whitrick stepped off the chair and hanged himself. As his face began to go blue, the chatroom users realized that it wasn't a sick joke. When the police arrived moments later (after a chatroom user called them), it was too late to save Whitrick...

Ridicule Mortis

Japan has seen the arrival of 'suicide clubs' in recent years where young Japanese talk online to find people to commit suicide with. Such bizarre networking has led to group suicides increasing in the country. Experts are troubled by such online communities because they are seen to actively encourage people to take their own lives. The term 'strength in numbers' has never had such a morbid ring to it...

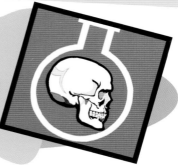